The story of a little dog who is larger than life.
Even when he's dead.

I AM NELSON

Martina Mars

Addendum
Publishing

First published in Great Britain in 2021 by Addendum Publishing

A catalogue record for this book is available from the British Library.

ISBN 978-1-8383675-0-3

Cover design by BespokeBookCovers.com
All photos & images, including cover photos, author's own collection.

www.addendumpublishing.co.uk

For Nelson.

Thousands of tiny little splinters of memories.

The way you look: all gleaming white, and I mean gleaming (someone once asked me if we were bleaching your fur to get that effect), but with an absolutely adorable flurry of tiny brown spots at the back of your ears and one big brown spot across your left eye (if we had been given a pound for every time someone asked us if your name was Patch, we would have been rich).

The way you move: always knowing exactly what you want and precisely where you want to go.

The way you eat: always anxious not to leave a single scrap of food behind.

The way you sleep: whimpering softly and chasing I don't know what in your dreams.

The way you always come running to me, whenever you're afraid or in pain, even though you're such a tough and fierce little boy.

Too many memories to mention them all. I will keep on clinging to every single one of them.

Thank you for letting me write this for you.

We love you, Baby Puppy, always, always and forever.

CONTENTS

Chapter 1

FIRST THINGS FIRST

Hello, I am Nelson!

My mum always used to say that I was somehow *more* than a dog, and I guess you could say that she was right.

They all say that I am dead now, but that doesn't make much sense to me. I've never felt more alive and how can you feel so alive when you're dead?

When I first got over here, everyone was really nice and tried to cuddle me, but as I once wrote to my Uncle Richard, they all learned the rule 'DON'T TOUCH MY BOTTOM! OR MY BACK!' soon enough. That's when I usually flash my teeth, because I REALLY hate when people try to touch me. I figure, why should they take liberties with me, when they don't touch and stroke anybody else they don't know.

I can't tell you much about where I am now, because it's not allowed and the pages just go blank when I talk about it. So I guess you'll just have to wait and see what it's like when you get here yourself. What I can say, is that it sucks that I can't be with my family anymore.

Well, I still am in a way, but now they can't seem to see me. I sometimes manage to visit them in their dreams, but that's just not enough. So I am not getting all the attention I want and I find that really frustrating.

I know that my mum and dad can feel me sometimes, but it makes them feel sad. I hate it when they cry, because I can't make it better by licking their faces like I used to.

Well I do it anyway, but it doesn't work in quite the same way as before. Now my pain is gone, I have so much more energy. But all I want is to be back again with my family.

I love my parents very, very much and they love me right back. My dad once calculated that my mum must have told me she loved me at least 20 times every single day of my life. That means she must have said it at least 80,280 times during the 11 years minus one day I lived with my parents. That's an awful lot of love, don't you think?

It was the first thing my mum would say to me in the morning and the last thing at night, and countless times in between. Every time she cuddled up to me on the sofa, every time she left again, and every time she passed me by on her way up or down the stairs. Every time she gave me my breakfast, my dinner or a treat. Every time she put my harness on to take me out for a walk, and once more (at least!) when she took it off again. She said it when she carried me up and down the stairs, and when she washed my paws. I had an 'I love you' for every time she found me doing anything funny or naughty, and she even said it when I flashed my teeth at her because I was in what she called 'one of my moods'. And sometimes she would say it just because and for no particular reason at all.

At times she says it even now that I'm gone, just not as often as before. My dad didn't say it out loud quite so often, but that's okay, because I know that he thought it all the time.

My parents are called Mummy and Papá. I know this, because they always used to ask me 'Where's

Mummy?' or 'Where's Papá?' when they wanted me to go and find them. They have other names too, and so did I, because my mum always invents new names for people she loves. She calls me *Baby Puppy* and *Poodle* (even though I look NOTHING like a poodle) and *Käsekuchen* (cheesecake) and *Mäuslein* (little mouse) and *Monsterle* (little monster) and many other silly names and surnames in different languages on different days. And I understand it all, because I can see the pictures in her mind when she says them. She even called me *Poochini* for a while, and *Placido Dogmingo*, when I went through one of my more laid-back phases. But most of the time, people who love me call me Nellie.

I should explain that my mum and dad are human, so they don't look like me. For starters, they have way less hair than I and they walk on their back legs all the time. But they are still my parents.

My mum never liked words like 'owner' or 'master' or 'pet'. She used to explain to people that although I wasn't human, I still was very much their son. Because parenthood doesn't depend on someone being the same race or species as their child. She said that being a parent simply means that you are responsible for someone physically and emotionally, that you care for them and love them unconditionally – which is precisely what my parents did for me. And that she didn't think she could have loved a human child any more than she loved me.

Mummy also hated when people said that animals can't think or feel, because it's just so obvious that we do. She thinks humans say that to make themselves feel superior, and to justify what they do to animals and plants. She says they just show their ignorance in doing so, because the truth is right there in front of your eyes if you care to look. To illustrate that point my mum always used to tell people the story of my brother Alfred and the fox.

It is a true story. I haven't made it up. And it goes like this:

Long before I was born, my brother Alfred, who was a Scottie dog, lived with my parents in London. I never got to know him as he died just before I was adopted. Each year around Christmas time, my parents would put up a Christmas tree with lights on it and baubles and other dangly bits and bobs.

I know, because they used to do the same for

me each year. And at the end, my mum always placed a small white toy deer under the tree. He was called Heloir. Now I personally didn't mind the deer, but apparently Alfred couldn't stand the sight of him. This might have had something to do with the fact that he tried to nip Heloir in the butt once or twice, and that Mummy had firmly told him off for it.

Anyway. The house where Alfred lived with my parents had a long garden which bordered onto a large cemetery. It was beautiful and quiet, and every now and then a fox would jump over the wall at the back and strut his stuff in the garden. He did this in plain view of Alfred, who stood foaming with anger by the glass patio doors and had to watch this parade helplessly, as he hadn't figured out how to open the doors by himself. Sometimes, however, my parents left the back door open, and then Alfred would rush outside and give chase to the fox. It has to be said that the fox was very agile, as foxes are, but Alfred unfortunately was not.

On many occasions the fox would run in a straight line in the direction of the garden shed and then sidestep like a dancer, leaving poor Alfred to almost plough head first into the shed because he couldn't change directions as easily. My mum says he looked like an angry rhino with fur and had the agility of a tanker.

Now, as much as Alfred hated the exchange, the fox simply *loooved* it. It provided him with all the entertainment he needed and he always finished the whole routine off by elegantly jumping up onto the shed roof. There he would lie for a while smiling, whilst Alfred was relegated to fuming and barking on the ground below.

Now, my parents were never quite sure why the fox did what he did next; whether he felt sorry for Alfred, or maybe wanted to say thank you for all the fun he had had, but one day he walked calmly into the garden, with a complete roast chicken in his mouth. I'm not sure where he got it from but my parents, who were watching from an upstairs window, saw the fox walk very slowly up the garden path, right up to the patio doors, looking at Alfred all the while, and then slowly laying down the chicken like a peace offering. Then he turned around and loped off to lie down on the roof of the shed to watch what would happen next.

Alfred couldn't believe it. For once he was in luck, as the back door had been left open. So he raced outside, nearly tripping over his own paws in his haste to get to the chicken. My dad says he then stopped and seemed to pause and think. Finally he picked up the chicken and vanished inside the house with it.

My mum says if that had been the whole story, it would have been quite extraordinary in itself, but that's not where the story ends.

She says the crafty little bugger, meaning my brother Alfred, must have wanted to reciprocate, to

7

show the fox that he didn't owe him anything. And what better way to achieve this than by getting rid of something at the same time, something he hated from the bottom of his heart.

So, to my parents utter amazement, they saw Alfred reappear a few minutes later with his own offering for the fox in his mouth. It was only when he laid it down, below where the fox was resting on the shed, that my parents finally saw what he had put down for the fox to take away in exchange for the chicken. And yes, you've guessed it: there, gleaming white in the grass lay Heloir. Needless to say, my mum raced down to the bottom of the garden to get him back. Oh, and poor Alfred didn't get his chicken either, as my parents were worried he might choke on the bones.

Also, there was the slight niggling doubt at the back of their minds that maybe, just maybe, the chicken had been poisoned, and the fox suspecting this, had brought it over to check and see if it would kill poor old Alfred.

I guess we will never know. But my parents realised that day that both Alfred and the fox did what they did knowing full well what they were up to, which just goes to show that animals are not as mindless as some people like to think.

Anyway, I wanted to tell you my story. But let me start right at the beginning. I'm just going to talk and my mum will pick it up in her head and write it down, like she always did whenever I wanted to send birthday or Christmas cards or letters to anyone. I even dictated a whole picture story to her once, when we came back from a holiday in Cornwall. But that's a story for later on.

Chapter 2

BEGINNINGS

I can't really remember my birth family at all, because I was very young when the other people gave me away. A medium once told my mum that my first mother rejected me, and that the first few months of my life had been very unhappy. And the people at the dog rescue centre, where I finally met my parents for the first time, told them that I had been abused by children, and that the people where I lived gave me up rather than discipline their children. I don't exactly know what 'abused' means, but I think it's something to do with why I was always so scared of exploding pellets and loud bangs and metal crutches and beer bottles. It's why I don't really trust anyone but my parents and my extended family.

Papá is a composer. He writes classical music. And before you ask, no, not the kind that sounds as if someone had dropped all the instruments of an orchestra on the floor and kicked them about. Or as if a cat was walking backwards and forwards across the keys of a piano. I know what that sounds like, I grew up with cats.

No, Papá writes beautiful music full of melodies. The kind of music that touches you and lifts you up; the kind that makes you want to smile or cry and sometimes both at the same time. The kind that makes you *feel*.

Often Mummy and I used to sit in his studio and listen to it. Some of it made her cry, but she always said they were happy tears, because the music moved her. I just sat and listened. Mostly on her lap, because then I felt more part of it all.

Also, because it was so much closer to the cookies Papá keeps in a glass jar on his desk for me. If I stared at it long enough, he would open the jar and give one to me. And if I stared VERY hard, he would laugh and give me another one.

Sometimes, when the music was very sad I used to cry too. Or when I didn't like it. Then I would howl like a wolf. For some reason the *Queen of the Night* aria from Mozart's *Magic Flute* always set me off. Oh, and any time I heard a recorder or an accordion playing. And if my mum sang very high notes, I always used to sing along with her. That usually made her stop and laugh, and then Papá used to say 'You're impossible, I can't write with all that noise going on!'

I still visit Papá in his studio, although he doesn't write much music at the moment. He says he doesn't feel like it because I'm gone. I still stare at the cookie jar, but now he can't seem to see me anymore. Although, sometimes I think my mum almost does. She looks down and talks to me and sometimes she strokes the air above me. I only wish she wouldn't cry so much, because I can't do anything to make her feel better. I often bark 'Look, Mummy, I'm here, I really am!' But she doesn't seem to hear me. And believe me, I have a very loud, insistent bark! That's the one thing my mum and dad say they really don't miss. Well, maybe only a little, because it was part of me.

13

I met my parents for the first time when I was just nine months old. I had been living in the kennels of the RSPCA in Brighton for a while. The people who work there took a funny photo of me and put it *on the line* or something. You know, so it appears on the thin metal boxes my parents have on their laps a lot when they work. They use them to write stuff and look at things, and Papá uses his to compose his music too.

Anyway, my mum saw my photo on hers when she was looking at dog rescue centres one day and sent it to Papá, because she loved the way I looked. Funny thing was, he then used it weeks later to make a birthday card for her, even though we had never met. Mummy still has the card in her box of treasured things.

But because my parents don't live in Brighton, they didn't come to see me straight away.

My mum is an actress, although she's resting quite a lot lately. Not literally, because she's always very busy, but that's apparently what actors do when they are female and grow older. It's not her choice and it makes her sad, because she loves what she does, but apparently you can't just act on your own.

I heard my mum say that a lot of people in her industry don't like to take chances on actors if they are not famous by a certain age. She says first you have to be right for a part. Then you have to be chosen by a casting director, who will ultimately decide if they want to introduce you to the director they work for. Unfortunately, a lot of casting directors only invite you to audition in the first place if they know your agent, which has nothing to do with your talent. So, even if you are really good at what you do, you might never get to meet the director or the producer of a film or play, just because you never get the chance to show them what you can do. The whole thing doesn't make much sense to me, because I almost always get to do what I want to do.

But I did meet a casting director once. Mummy's agent had been asked if my mum had a dog, and if yes, could she please bring it to the casting. So up we went to London and I got to go on the Underground, too, for the first time.

My mum says she learned three things on that trip. Firstly, that I was claustrophobic. Secondly, that I didn't like casting directors. And thirdly, never to take me to an audition again. That's partly because I didn't take well to being called 'Ben' as per the script and therefore refused to react in any way shape or form, but mainly because I tried to nip the casting director, which forced my mum to instantly demonstrate her acting skills in a big way.

As in 'Oh, how weird, he's never done that before!' Needless to say, we didn't get the job.

Anyway, back to my story.

At the time when I was at the RSPCA rescue centre, Mummy was working a lot, mainly in the film studios around London. Then, all of a sudden out of the blue she got a phone call from her agent, saying that she had been offered work on a commercial, which was meant to be filmed on the roller coaster on the pier in Brighton of all places.

Now my mum believes in signs and she took that as a BIG sign, especially as Papá was free that day to accompany her. So they finally rang the RSPCA and asked if they could see me afterwards. I had a different name back then, but I'm not going to tell you what it was, because it brings back bad memories and I don't want to keep them.

On the day my parents came to see me for the very first time, my dad made my mum promise that they would only adopt me if I clearly showed a connection to them from the start.

It was a beautiful day, with bright, blue skies and oh so many good smells in the air. At visiting time, I saw a man and a woman walking up the kennels holding hands, and that's when I got rather excited, because somehow I just knew that they were looking for me and that everything would be different from now on. I just knew that this time it was going to be forever and I wouldn't be brought back like twice before.

My mum tells it like this:

'We had just arrived at the RSPCA dog rescue centre in Brighton and were very excited to meet, what we had been told, was a very shy, little, white dog, Jack Russell mixed with Corgi, with pointy, spotted ears and a brown patch over his left eye. The first thing we noticed, when we saw him for the first time, was that he didn't look as funny and awkward as in his photo. He was much slimmer and WAY more active than we had imagined. He was also decidedly not shy. He was barking his head off along with all the other dogs and was raring to leave his kennel. He was wearing a protective collar around his neck to stop him from licking himself, as he had just been neutered the day before. As soon as his protective collar came off and he was on a lead, he started to pull with all his might. He was so strong that we could barely hold on to him.

He pulled us right down to the exercise ground and

17

was hell-bent on catching up with the bigger dogs, leaving the smaller ones in his wake. He simply wouldn't stop pulling, so my husband turned around to me and said: 'Amor, remember that we promised each other that we wouldn't adopt him if he doesn't show any connection to us? I really don't think this dog is linking with us.'

And that's when the weirdest thing happened. The little white dog simply stopped dead the very second he said this. From pulling at what seemed like 100 miles per hour to NOT. AT. ALL. And then he turned around and jumped up and put his paws on our legs. First on mine, then on my husband's.

I remember thinking that it was really strange how he seemed to be making sure that he was doing it to both of us.

And then he kissed and licked our hands and wagged his long tail like mad to say hello.

And that's when we knew. We simply knew that he was ours. And we looked into his incredibly clever brown eyes, and we noticed for the first time that he had brown eyelashes on one and white eyelashes on the other, and we fell in love.'

What I didn't know was that the people at the rescue centre had asked my parents to put me back into my kennel after our walk, whilst they completed the adoption paperwork. So I REALLY panicked, because I thought they didn't want me after all. Mum told Auntie Dee a few days later that I had let my tail droop as they were putting me back inside. She also said that I had nudged her hand to make sure she put my protective collar back on before she closed the gate, and that it had almost made her cry, because she couldn't explain to me that they would be back in a few minutes to pick me up for good.

All I know is that Mummy and Papá did come back, just when I was about to give up hope. And boy, was I happy! But it did make me worry for a long time, and every time they put me in our car I was frantic, because I always thought they were going to drive me right back to the kennels.

It took me quite a long time to get over my fear. In fact, one day I hyperventilated so badly that my dad had to stop the car right on the hard shoulder of the M25 motorway to calm me down. Mummy then put me on her lap and stroked me until I was able to breathe normally again.

After that my parents came up with the brilliant plan to always give me treats whenever they took me somewhere by car. Boy, did that work! I LOVED going everywhere by car after that.

Chapter 3

FAMILY AND FRIENDS

Let me tell you about my extended family.

Well, there are my Auntie Dee and my Uncle Vini, who I've known almost since the moment my parents adopted me, and who have been around during most of the important moments of my life. I love them a lot and they are the closest family I've got apart from my mum and dad. I always got to stay with them whenever my parents had to go away abroad and couldn't take me with them.

The first time this happened, my mum called Auntie Dee loads from Greece, because she was so worried about me. She would have called her even more often, but she didn't want to get on my auntie's nerves. But all was well, as my aunt and uncle loved me, too. And my Uncle Vini always made sure I got LOADS of extra food and treats, even though I wasn't technically allowed to have them. I loved hanging out with him and not just because of the food. I also licked his face and shaven head a lot, especially in the morning, to get him going.

Uncle Vini manages a shop. Shame I could never visit him there, because they have tons of yummy food on all the shelves. But unfortunately dogs are not allowed inside. Uncle Vini also loves to paint. He even painted me a few times, and two of my portraits are now hanging in our house. One in the living room, and the other one in Papá's studio, so I can still hear and see what's going on.

Sometimes I see my parents talk to the pictures as if I was there. And of course I am, just not inside the paintings. Not all of the time anyway.

Auntie Dee is very clever and loves to study and learn new things. She's always finding out about ways to make things better for the community and the environment.

She and Mummy took me once to the garden where Auntie Dee volunteers. I had a good rummage around and was tempted to pee on a rather large pumpkin, but my mum stopped me just in time.

I was already a bit older when I met my Uncle Richard and my Auntie Marina for the first time.

Uncle Richard is a historical novelist and has written many books about kings and queens. Three of them were published all around the world and he has two more manuscripts lying under his bed in an old suitcase whilst he's waiting to hear if anyone wants to print them.

Mummy says Uncle Richard is a walking encyclopaedia, as he knows everything about history you can imagine, dates and facts and all. His house is lovely and old and full of amazing things from the past – including a few ghosts that come and go. And some of the floors are crooked and creak. I used to hang out there whenever my mum took me with her to do stuff *on the line* for him.

I used to walk in, wipe myself on the hand towel in his bathroom, and then race upstairs and sit on the sofa next to my mum. Sometimes, I got a bit impatient if it took her too long, and then I would stare at her until she got the drift and took me back home.

And at the front door I would always try to get

at Uncle Richard's post that the annoying postman had put in a metal cage. I remember one time I got really irate about it and my uncle decided to let me have the junk mail to calm me down.

You can believe me, I made short shrift of it in no time at all! It took me no more than three seconds flat to shred the lot. And then of course Uncle Richard wasn't allowed to touch or clean the mess away.

I don't like people touching my things. Whether it's paper, my all-nightly carrots (even the bits I spit out and won't eat anymore), or even my own vomit.

The rule is: once it's on the floor, it's mine. And you better not touch it! My mum says I'm almost as fast as a piranha when it comes to enforcing that rule. And believe me, quite a few people have the scars to prove it.

Did I mention that I had firm, but different, rules for different people? Uncle Richard for example was allowed to kiss me. Most of the time. If he overdid it, I had to stop him by flashing my teeth. Worked every time.

Mostly, though, I licked his beard to say hello, especially on Sunday afternoons, when we all met up at Auntie Marina's for tea, coffee and cake. But he was NEVER allowed to touch me uninvited. Especially not my bottom. I'm not ashamed to say that I once snapped at him when he forgot himself. That doesn't mean that I didn't love him, because I did, it was just, well, my rules.

Now Auntie Marina was a different story. She could touch me all day long. That's because she was a lady and very calm. Also, I guess, because she used to run a school and knows how to deal with unruly children.

She lives in this beautiful house overlooking the sea and I went to visit her often. I still do, and I swear she feels me sometimes.

Like Uncle Richard she also has a ghost, which I used to see in the far corner of her living room, just behind one of her big armchairs, whenever there was a full moon.

Auntie Marina bought me lovely toys and even a day bed for when I was ill. And every time I was at her house for a visit, I used to bark until she got up to give me a treat.

In fact, the routine went like this. My mum or dad would ring the doorbell to let Auntie Marina know we were there. And that was the signal for me to start barking until they opened the front door. If they took too long, I had to scratch the door to hurry them up. Then I would run up the stairs and nose a quick hello to Auntie Marina, before positioning myself firmly in front of her antique secretaire desk, where all my treats and toys were housed. Still barking at the top of my voice of course. Until she gave me a treat, which I then hid somewhere inside her house for later use.

You know, after I died, a visiting dog found my last treat, where I had hidden it under the cushion of a chair. It made Auntie Marina very sad. But for some reason the other dog could see me when I warned him off my treat. I scared him so much that he pooped all over the floor. Serves him right, the thief!

By the way, it was Uncle Richard who taught me the rule 'Bark, bark and you shall get'. And so I did.

For treats. For attention. But mostly for cake. And no amount of shouting 'Stop it, Nellie!' would ever shut me up. Especially not when I wanted to play pull. My favourite pastime when Uncle Richard was around.

I used to bring him my ball, which was technically a rubber turtle, and bark until he finally grabbed the neck end hanging out of my mouth. I would then pull with all my might, growling all the while, as in fact did he – only much louder than me – until Auntie Marina used to shout that she couldn't hear a single word that was being said anymore. And then Uncle Richard would pull me close to kiss me on the nose, whilst I was hanging on to my ball for dear life, always careful not to touch me with his hands, because by now he knew my rules. And then suddenly he would let go, pretending that I was stronger than him, because Papá had once told him to always let me win so I would feel good about myself. Now I am quite sure that I would have won anyway. For one because I have very good teeth, and for another because I am very muscular and very strong and heavy or – as my mum put it – I seemed to have cement in my behind.

Did I mention that I have two grandmas? They both lived in other countries, so they only came to visit us occasionally. I loved them both in different ways because they are very different people.

And… um… I bit them both, too. For different

reasons. And then had to apologise.

Grandma Olga told Mummy that I repented right after I bit her, which is true. I can't really remember why I bit her, probably just because I was in a bad mood that day. But I did feel very sorry afterwards and made sure I cuddled up to her to let her know that. And I sat on her lap a lot when she let me near her again, just to make her feel special. Because normally I only sit on Mummy's lap and only when I want to. But in this case I made an exception because I knew I had misbehaved.

Grandma Olga is Papá's mum and she lived in Argentina. She used to come and visit us together with Papá's sister Pachy every two years or so, and stay in our house for a few months during the winter. We hung out a lot together on the sofa and we sometimes still do now because she died just four months after I did, and now sometimes comes over to make sure my parents are okay.

The same goes for Mummy's grandparents, who I never met when they were still alive. I only met them after I died. Whenever they come over these days, my parents can smell them. Not because they stink, but because they bring the smell of their old house with them when they do, and Mummy and Papá recognise it.

My mum's mum is called Grandma C. She doesn't really look and behave like a typical grandma, so my mum only calls her grandma just for fun. She used to live in Italy, but now she lives in Germany, and I met her for the first time when I was just about a year old. At that time I was still on my best behaviour, because I was still worried that I would end up back at the rescue centre if I wasn't nice to everyone. So we cuddled a lot and she was even allowed to put my harness on and take me for long walks along the beach by herself.

Unfortunately for her, by the time I met her the last time, I had long figured out that my parents loved me no matter what and would never give me up. So I could finally show my true personality and lay down some ground rules. And as I've said before, rule number one was: 'DON'T TOUCH MY BOTTOM! OR MY BACK! Or only when I want you to and then only for precisely how long I want you to.' Now, Grandma C had been warned about this, but I guess to be fair the second clause got sometimes a bit confusing for people because I could change my mind at the speed of lightning.

So that time I bit her, I had sidled along the sofa and placed my back right under her hand to signal that it was okay to touch me for now, and that stroking and petting was very much required. So she obliged quite happily.

Such a shame that she didn't realise when I wanted her to stop…

I REALLY got told off for that incident and I very much regret that she never dared to touch me again after that. She still has a little scar on the back of her hand to remind her of me. If you read this, Grandma C: I am really sorry!

And then there's my Auntie Pachy. She's really special and great fun and very caring, and her and Mummy are not just sisters-in-law, but great friends too. I really liked her and I only told her off when she was teasing me too much.

Well, I may have tried to nip her, too, on one occasion. But she was wriggling her finger at my nose at the time and making fun of me for flashing my teeth at her.

I used to do that a lot. My mum says she always knew when I did it in public, because people used to burst out laughing as we walked past them. It was my way of making sure nobody would dare to touch me. I wouldn't growl or bark or any of the sort. Waste of energy in my opinion. Just a quick flash of my teeth would neatly do the trick.

It was quite different from when I used to smile. And yes, of course I can smile! I don't know why people think dogs can't smile. We do, because we know that's what *you* do when you're happy. I used to do it in the mornings after I had climbed into bed with my parents, and to let them know I appreciated my good morning treats and cuddles. And I most certainly did it every time Mummy and Papá and Auntie Dee and Uncle Vini got together.

If you don't believe me, have a look at the photos my parents have collected to remember me by.

Somebody else I really appreciated, even though they didn't know it at the time, were my aunties Barbara and Margaret. They lived just two doors down from us and they were very kind to me when I stayed over on a few occasions, when my parents were away and Auntie Dee and Uncle Vini couldn't look after me. They were so lovely to me, they even moved their living room sofa to the window, so I could look out to sea just like at home.

Unfortunately... um... they too got the sharp end of my teeth on a few occasions, when I mistook their putting on my harness for taking liberties. I'm sorry about that now, especially as Auntie Barbara always brought me lots of yummy treats each Saturday.

Mummy was really embarrassed about my

behaviour and apologised a lot, but Auntie Barbara was quite practical about it and simply bought herself a pair of thick gloves for whenever she had to handle me. And my mum bought me a soft harness I could leave on the whole time during my stay with my aunties. That way nobody had to fear for their hands and nobody had to touch my back and tummy to put it on.

Auntie Barbara used to always put her gloves on when it was time to go for a walk and then fish real fast for the hook on my harness, to attach my lead to it before I could swivel around to stare and snarl at her and dare her to touch me some more.

During my time with my aunties, I taught them exactly what I wanted and when I wanted it. I took them for long walks, insisting they both come along at the same time. And I always got to choose where we went, too. They were very accommodating and didn't mind that I was in charge. Not much anyway.

Of course not everybody liked me. In fact quite a few people didn't, but that never bothered me. I remember one winter, friends of my parents sent a Christmas card addressed to them 'and the most vicious dog in the Old Town'. Now, that might have had something to do with the fact that I tumbled their dogs on one occasion and barked at them most of the other times we met, but I took it as quite a compliment.

Chapter 4

OTRO LINDO DÍA

I remember the day when my parents brought me home for the first time as if it was yesterday: the trip there in the car on my mum's lap, whilst my dad was driving, the white house with the cavalier statue on top, right by the sea.

I felt like the luckiest dog alive. I remember meeting Auntie Barbara and Auntie Margaret from two doors down for the first time, as we were getting out of the car, and then running like mad up the many stairs of my new home to check it all out.

I don't remember peeing all over the sofa in the living room in my excitement, but my parents do. I never did it again, not even when I was ill and the vet gave me medicine that made me pee all the time. But that was far in the future and for now I was finally home.

I loved our house the second I saw it. It was even nicer than what I had hoped it would be, when I was still dreaming of my forever home back at the rescue centre. It had three floors for us and another one for guests, and staircases going up and down in a spiral, and loads of windows I could look out of during the day when my parents were working and couldn't take me places.

I had the choice of one window in my dad's studio, one in our bedroom (yes, of course from on top of my parents' bed – their rule of 'No dogs on the bed' went straight out of that very window on day one), and two further windows in the living room. The window to the far right of the room was my favourite by far. I used to climb up onto the top of the sofa, which gave me the perfect height to check out what was going on in the streets below.

I spent one day short of 11 years controlling my territory that way. And of course making my displeasure known at the top of my voice, should a dog or person I didn't like walk too closely past our house. People got used to seeing me there, and during the summer season plenty of them took my picture as they passed by. You could even see the sea from my window. And because our sofa was HUGE and went around the corner, which gave me access to the other window, I could stretch myself out full-length and lounge around like a sloth among the many cushions.

And wherever I went I left a trail of snowy white hair. I heard my mum tell a friend that before I had come to live with my parents, there had been a cream-coloured carpet covering all the floors, which they then removed as part of their renovations. And no sooner had they painted the floorboards a black-brown colour, I came along. And with it my white hair. Tons of it. So the floors looked more or less as if the carpet hadn't been removed after all. Well, almost.

My mum could never fathom how I could produce so much hair without going bald. She filled vacuum bag after vacuum bag with the stuff. And she said that if she'd spun it, she could have knitted several jumpers with it during my lifetime.

My hair went positively everywhere and stuck to everything like super glue. It even ended up in Germany on the sofa of Auntie Dee's parents, and I had never been to visit them. Somehow my hair must have travelled there in my auntie's suitcase. It also turned up in Argentina during one of my parents' visits to Auntie Pachy. And no, I had never been to her house either.

Uncle Richard once made the mistake of wearing black trousers when he came over for a visit. He made that mistake only once. He didn't really sit that long on our sofa, but he did find out the hard way, that black clothes and I don't match. Apparently he spent hours after his visit trying to get rid of the white film of hair covering every inch of his trousers.

My parents themselves started to wear lighter and lighter colours in the end, and Mummy even bought a white hoodie for Papá, because whenever they were wearing darker colours, it looked as if they had been caught in a fur storm. You should have seen my dad's black socks. Or should I say – his formerly black socks.

Every now and again he would buy new ones for a concert, which he then put in an airtight container until they were to be used. Once. And then they were relegated to the box with all the other fur covered socks. Even now that I'm gone, my hair still turns up in the most surprising places. I guess it's my way of reminding everyone that I'm still around.

But back to my very first day with my new family.

On the way to my new home, my parents bought a soft donut bed just for me, which they put in their bedroom so I could always sleep with them.

Oh, and just before we went to sleep for the first time together, they gave me a goodnight doggie biscuit. I couldn't believe my luck and almost didn't dare to eat it. Just in case I was imagining things.

From that night on, for the rest of my life, I always got my cookie at night and I will never forget how happy it made me. On the odd occasion I had to remind my parents to give it to me, but not very often. Of course, often after Mummy had given it to me, I pretended she hadn't when Papá came upstairs, in order to get another one.

This worked particularly well when they were both a bit stressed from working and couldn't quite remember whether they had already given me a treat or not. When they finally cottoned on to the fact that I was doing this on purpose, it made them laugh a lot, so I would get my second cookie anyway. Papá used to say 'Life's too short' and he was right.

In the morning, when I woke up in my new bed for the very first time with my new parents beside me, Mummy turned round and smiled at me and said 'Otro lindo día!'. That's Spanish and means 'another beautiful day'.

And for a very long time, both my parents used to say it to me whenever we woke up, just to let me know that we were having such a good time together, and that everything was going to be just fine. And that every day from now on was going to be another beautiful day.

So when I heard my mum say to my dad a few days ago that now that I'm gone, there would be no more *lindo días,* it made me very sad.

Before my parents adopted me, my mum had asked the lovely lady from the RSPCA, who got to decide whether it would be okay for me to live with them, whether it would be possible to change my name, as she had noticed that I didn't like the one the other people had given me.

She was told that it was fine, and that it would take about a week or so for me to recognise it as my new name and to react to it. Well, I guess the lady didn't know me very well.

So my mum sat down on the sofa and made a HUGE list of possible names, which she then ran past my dad. After a few hours they narrowed it down to two. Would you believe that I almost ended up being called Errol?! As in Errol Flynn, the actor – Mummy rather liked the swashbuckling connection. Also, because the name has an 'e' in it. My mum sees letters as colours and the letter 'e' apparently fits me.

In the end, my parents decided that it would be too difficult a name to shout out loud because of the 'r's in it, and so I became who I was always meant to be – Nelson.

And guess what? It took a grand total of ONE call for me to react to my new name. Because of course I had always known that I was Nelson.

After they gave me my name, my parents took me for a long walk to show me the surrounding area. We went up 178 steps and ended up on a green hill just behind my new home. I *loooooved* it! I ran around like mad as soon as we got there and never wanted to stop. Then I rolled over in the grass until I got all tangled up in my new lead. Unfortunately the first dog we met bit me just above the eye, which freaked my parents out because they thought they had jinxed me by naming me Nelson. My eye was fine in the end, but I heard them say that my namesake Admiral Nelson had lost the sight in one eye and wore an eye patch just like me. Little did they know that many years later I was going to lose my right arm just like him, too.

But for now, everything was fine and I was having the time of my life.

Chapter 5

EARLY DAYS

For the first three weeks of my life with them, my parents didn't leave me home alone at all, which was super-duper great. During that time, however, they happened to get a dinner invitation from some lovely people they know, who live just up the road from us. So, as my mum and dad didn't want to leave me behind, they asked if I could tag along, and were told it would not be a problem.

Biiig mistake as it turned out!

I'll let my mum tell you the story in her own words:

'We arrived at our friends' flat, Nelson in tow. Their own dogs had been locked away in the kitchen to avoid any doggie dramas, so we thought all was well. Nelson of course was very curious and wanted to explore the place.

Our hosts had also invited another couple along, so there were six of us who didn't really know each other very well. Also, because we were relatively new in town and quite unsure about the dress code of the affair, we had made an effort, which saw me sporting a rather short dress with very high heels. Not a terribly wise decision in light of what transpired next.

So, anyway, in struts Nelson and starts to sniff everything and to make himself at home. He walks around, checks everything out, even has a brief excursion into the garden, then comes back, unceremoniously and without warning cocks his leg and proceeds to pee all over the antique rug in front of the dining table. As the other guests were already seated and about to begin eating their starters, you can imagine this caused quite a stir.

I immediately jumped up and ran to the kitchen to get some paper towels to get rid of the mess, and to quite frankly apologise at least a dozen times to our hosts. I then raced back and frantically started to wipe the floor and – bearing in mind that my skirt was rather minuscule and my heels extremely high – tried very hard indeed not to expose myself whilst doing this.

In the end I just about managed it without flashing my knickers all over the place, and everyone was just about to start eating again, when Nelson, looking me squarely in the eye, squats down and starts to follow the pee with a humongous poo. On the antique rug.

Now, mortified doesn't even begin to describe what we felt!

Suffice to say, that we moved at the speed of

lightning to get rid of the second mess.

But luckily for us, the whole episode was then, in true British fashion, neatly swept under the soiled rug and never mentioned again. And nobody said a word, when halfway through the dinner, Nelson happened to help himself to a toy, which he then noisily proceeded to shake to death under the dinner table for about half an hour or so.'

All *I* remember is that we never went back there. My mum says that to add insult to injury, I would always make sure to growl or bark at their friends and their dogs, whenever I met them in the street or on the beach afterwards.

And so my new life with my parents began. In the beginning everything was new to me. But I'm a quick learner and I figured things out pretty quickly. I learned that humans brush their teeth (and occasionally mine, too), that they pee and poo inside a white, shiny bowl, but luckily didn't expect me to do the same. That they sit down to eat two to three times per day and will share their food with you, if you stare at them long and hard enough and/or whine, and that if you played your cards right, you could get countless treats in between. That eating one's blanket wasn't such a great idea (for them – because I thought it was amazing fun!), and that when people sing it doesn't mean they're in pain and need urgent rescuing.

And eventually I learned that when you are loved, you get to do more and more things your own way and you can put down some rules of your own, without fear of being thrown out. Over the years I came up with quite a few of them, believe you me!

I established my rule number one, 'Don't touch my bottom! Or my back!' when I was approximately two years old. It was right after my last vaccination at the vet's.

I remember him stroking my back all the way down to my bottom, which was rather nice and comforting. And then, without warning, he all of a sudden sneakily plunged a needle into my bottom. I yelped out loud because it hurt a lot – and not just my pride. I felt betrayed and simply couldn't believe he had done that. And that's when I decided there and then, that I would NEVER EVER trust anyone again to touch me where I couldn't see it. With the exception of my parents, Auntie Dee, Uncle Vini, Auntie Marina and very, very, *very* few others.

Sadly that meant that even people I really liked and respected, and even some who I knew quite well, would never be allowed touch me again. If they valued their hands.

People like the two Richards, who I first met at Auntie Marina's and really liked a lot; Jean, and Ian, whose shoes I attacked (whilst he was wearing them); and Barbara, who works with Mummy and Papá at the theatre he runs, and who, I have to say, was very good indeed at keeping her hands to herself at all times.

Even people I had known for years, such as John, who was a cobbler and *the* go-to place in the Old Town if you were a dog. He would always stop working as soon as he saw you and cuddle and stroke you, and then feed you treats until you were almost sick. Dogs loved him so much that whenever they got lost, they would make their way to John's rather than go home.

It really made John sad when I established rule number one, but I just couldn't help myself. Still took the treats, mind, but never let him touch me again.

And as for anyone else – *especially* the vet – it was hands off forever after that.

Another rule of mine had to do with possessions. As time went by, I began to realise that all the toys were mine, the food in the lower cupboard of the kitchen was mine, hell, stuff on the floor was mine, the sofa was DEFINITELY mine, in fact the whole house was mine, and of course my parents were mine.

And don't you ever forget it!

I guess you could say that I took the rule of all stuff on the floor being mine a bit too far at times, as I have actually been known to have bitten guests for putting their own shoes back on. Oops.

Finally I had everything I ever dreamed of. My parents made sure I didn't want for anything. I had toys galore and everyone continuously added to them. My Auntie Marina even gave me a strategy game once to stimulate my brain. Not that it needed stimulating, but hey, I did her the favour and worked it out in no time to oohs and aahs of the whole family.

I even had some clothes – not particularly dignified, but useful in the rain or snow. Especially my parka with the hood and my raincoat. Oh, and I had various costumes for various festivals, too. Wasn't too keen on them, but since my parents also dressed up, I went along with it. I quite liked my pirate outfit though, complete with flintlock pistol strapped to my back. That was always a crowd pleaser and lots of people took photos of me on Pirate Day. I was less convinced by my various Halloween outfits, although I guess the skeleton T-shirt was fun.

I also had blankets and pillows and eventually I even got my own proper bed. And I mean *proper* bed, as in with surrounding headboard and four feet. My parents were rather excited when they presented it to me, but I wasn't too keen on it because I rather liked my donut bed, the one my parents bought me on the day they adopted me.

So then they tried to convince me to use my new bed by putting me into it and cooing to me. Insulting, or what?! They still hadn't learned yet that I know EXACTLY what I want. I always have. And what I wanted wasn't the new bed. That's for sure.

The next thing my parents tried was to bribe me with treats. As in, 'Look, Nellie, how nice your new bed is! You even get treats if you sleep in here!' But of course I wasn't going to fall for that one, because by then I knew I was going to get the treats no matter what. They tried and tried and I just kept resisting. Until at last they gave up. I heard them say they were going to give the bed away the next day, as I didn't like it. And that's when I decided that I wanted the new bed after all. Jumped right into it, lay down and never ceased to use it. Until I got ill. But that's another story.

My life was such fun. I discovered new things

every single day. Some things I could have guessed, others shocked or simply surprised me. One of the things that REALLY surprised me, was finding out that my poo was worth a lot. Must have been, the way my parents always quickly ran to bag it.

And not just *my* poo. Any dog poo. I often watched people on the beach desperately looking for it and getting rather upset if they spoiled it by stepping on it. That's why I always made sure to point out with a nod where I had left mine.

We went for endless walks and I discovered that I liked sticks and branches a lot. The bigger the better. Sometimes I chose branches that were so big and heavy I could hardly carry them. That didn't stop me though. The only tricky bit was to manoeuvre the branch past the legs of people in front of you whilst going at full tilt.

Didn't always work out as I intended it to. So then you would hear a smack, followed by a loud yelp, as someone's calves connected with the branch.

Another great game was to chase sticks when they were thrown for me. I always preferred my dad to throw them, because when my mum throws stuff you never know where it will land. Seriously!

I loved chasing and carrying sticks up on the hill and in the woods, but down on the beach I discovered my love for pebbles and stones.

It happened quite by accident. Someone threw a stone – can't remember who – I ran, found it and brought it back. Didn't GIVE it back, mind, just CARRIED it back and kept it. And from that moment on I was hooked. Barked my head off, too, if people didn't want to play. And I got REALLY good at finding them. It took my parents quite some time to realise just how good I was at it. I think it was my Auntie Pachy who threw a stone too far, and as it landed in the water and I wasn't in the mood to get my paws wet, we left it behind.

A few hours later when the tide had gone out again, we were back on the beach and I finally went to fetch the stone my auntie had thrown. Seemed normal to me, but you should have heard the hoo-ha that broke out when everyone realised that I had found the exact same stone Auntie Pachy had thrown into the sea earlier on. I think they noticed some marking or other on the stone that proved it had been hers, among the thousands of pebbles on our beach.

And that's when they tested the theory. For hours. They marked and threw stone after stone, further and further away, and I found every single one of them. Of course! I mean, why wouldn't I??!!! They even tried not to touch the stone for more time than it took to quickly scoop it up and throw it, to prevent their scent marking the stone. My mum reckoned around one second or so. Didn't matter, I still found it.

After that we played that particular game for years and I never tired of it. Even when I had to run on three legs, which I didn't mind, as long as I still got to play 'find the pebble'.

It only got tiring for my parents when they wanted to swim and relax on the beach. Because I didn't. Too many pebbles, too little time.

Chapter 6

THINGS I LOVE

I loved going for walks. Any time of day or night. The first time my parents let me off the lead was roughly two months after they had adopted me. I remember that my Grandma C had come over for a visit, and her and my parents took me for a long walk through the Country Park behind our house.

Up and down we went, over the hills, past the creek and the gnarly trees my mum says remind her of Middle Earth.

We ended up on a nudist beach and had a picnic. I didn't take off any clothes and neither did my parents, but some other people did. I had never seen naked people wandering about with nothing but their boots on. So I tried to nip the dangly bits of a guy who happened to walk past my mouth, which made him squeal in anticipation and my parents blush with embarrassment. They apologised a lot to him, even though I hadn't gotten hold of anything yet.

I *looooved* my food! I couldn't wait until it was being served each mealtime. In the morning I used to have my breakfast on my own, as my parents don't really eat any. Or at least not very often. Then, at lunchtime, they used to have sandwiches together around 12pm and of course I knew exactly when that was. My inner clock is excellent.

In the evenings at around 5pm, my mum would start to cook dinner. My favourite meal of the whole day! I anticipated it all day long and woe betide anyone who tried to delay my parents from coming home on time for it. I used to stand and stare at them with my meanest expression on my face until they gave in and got the food going.

Uncle Richard and Auntie Marina remember many a time on Sundays, when I used to will my parents telepathically to make us leave my aunt's place at 5pm on the dot. And got rather irate if they didn't take the hint at once.

Now my parents aren't very formal, and as I

was part of the family, I got to sit next to the table in my basket whenever they ate. I know from some of my doggie friends that most people don't like their dogs or cats near them when they eat, because they think it's not very hygienic. And that they teach them not to beg for food and don't give them any during human mealtimes.

I never understood why that is, and luckily my parents didn't either. Mind you, whenever they had dinner guests who weren't really close family, they used to pretend that I wasn't allowed to either. They always made it up to me afterwards though.

In later years, when my parents carried me down to the kitchen in my travel bed because I couldn't walk down the stairs by myself anymore, I used to copy the way they sat, i.e. flat on my bum, ramrod straight back, legs stretched out to the sides, which made Mummy giggle because I am rather long, and she thought I looked like an upright, overgrown sausage with legs.

My mum really loves cooking, because she says it's creative and calms her nerves. But never mind that – it's the result that counts.

I used to stand by the staircase and sniff around

the corner to check what was on the menu each night. I loved almost all the things she cooked. Maybe one or two dishes I wasn't so keen on, but on the whole it was great. Especially Goulash and Sauerkraut (I know, weird, but I could have eaten tons of the stuff), sausages, and spaghetti (we reckon, that's my Papá's genes coming through – mind you he likes his with olive oil, whereas Mummy and I prefer them with tomato sauce). I think my favourite food was roast chicken with roast vegetables. I sometimes cried with joy when I detected that was on the menu.

My dad would usually lay the table, although I rather would have preferred him not to, because he has this habit of randomly dropping stuff. I had to jump out of the way on many occasions to avoid being clobbered by falling forks or knives. And even when nothing was dropped, I was always ducking and diving in anticipation of stuff hitting the floor. In the end I stayed well clear when he was in the kitchen. Just in case.

And always the best moment was when my mum finally finished cooking and shouted 'Comida!' (that's food in Spanish) up to me and my dad, to let us know that dinner was ready. When I still could, I used to race downstairs as soon as I heard that.

But in the last year of my life, when I had to be carried downstairs, I used to run over to my dad to stop him from working, and if he didn't react THAT VERY SECOND, I would bark at him at the top of my voice to get him going.

Once we were in the kitchen, I would quickly gulp down most of my own food so that I had nothing left and therefore a good reason to beg for what I really wanted to eat. And of course my parents obliged.

My mum and dad always used to buy me a hamburger for my birthdays. Each year I used to wait with Mummy by the picnic benches near the beach, while Papá went to get my birthday take-away. Unless of course it rained, and then we did it all at home. I was always allowed up on the picnic table, where I prepared to wolf my burger down and then get more titbits from my parents as they ate their own.

They invariably used to photograph the whole event, and I was quite happy to pose as I always did, when anyone pointed a camera at me. Mummy says it's because I inherited her acting genes somehow.

Some years I was simply too fast for them, and all the pictures show is a before and after shot of me with and without the hamburger.

It was Uncle Richard who decided to give me a steak birthday dinner every year. This was usually hosted at our house and Auntie Marina came over, too.

Uncle Richard always tells the story of how he went to the butcher's in town to buy the steaks, and that he told the man serving him that it was for me. Apparently the butcher exclaimed: 'What? For a dog? But this is a special steak!' To which my Uncle Richard replied: 'Yes, but it's for a special dog!'

See how well he knew me!

I also LOVED *mimo*! That's Spanish for a cuddle. I taught my parents that's what I wanted whenever I made a specific mewling sound. I had them well trained. Especially my mum who could never resist it. She used to laugh and then kiss me all over. And nibble my ears. She did it for years and then couldn't believe her own eyes when she saw me copying her way of ear nibbling on a Labrador in the park. (And neither could the Labrador.)

She also used to sniff me. She told Papá she absolutely adored my smell. Whenever Mummy cuddled me she would suddenly stop and ask '*Más mimo?*' to find out if I wanted more. And I would mewl to say that YES, OF COURSE I wanted more. Sometimes Papá would shout from upstairs, 'Not again!' and 'I can still hear you!' to make Mummy laugh. Because she loved her *mimos*, too.

I miss my *mimos* now I'm dead. And so does she. A lot.

I also miss playtime with my dad each night. I used to watch him like a hawk all day long, and the very second he finally put down his work, I would race over to the box with my toys, quickly choose one and bring it over to him. I never got tired of it. We played pull and had lots of play fights, whereby I locked his arm down by crossing my front legs over and around it so that he couldn't move, and then furiously licking and nibbling his hand and fingers until my tongue almost went numb. I could have done that forever. I even did it when I only had three legs. Because my right front leg was missing by then, I couldn't really lock Papá's arm down as before. But I sure tried. And he pretended it still worked to make me feel better.

Another thing I really loved was to go on holiday with my mum and dad. Because it meant that I had their undivided attention at last. Every second of every day. Perfect! We stayed right here in the UK for that because if my parents had wanted to take me abroad, I would have needed a passport to do so. That's because we live on an island. And it would have meant lots of injections and extra trips to the vet.

Luckily for me, my parents knew that I hated vets and needles. Also, my mum said that she didn't really like so many chemicals floating around in my system, because she read somewhere that it could take years off my life. As it turns out cancer did that all by itself anyway and all the care in the world couldn't stop it.

She always said that that was rather ironic.

So we went camping instead. All over the country over the years. Sometimes we stayed in a tent and sometimes in a static caravan. When my parents first took me, I had never seen a tent before. I got to watch them erect it from the back of our car. I simply couldn't believe my eyes. It was HUGE and blue and as soon as it was up, I got to explore it to my heart's content. (More like roll around in it for hours on end.) Only at nights I found it a bit spooky because the wind kept moving the walls, and the rain sounded so much louder when it hit the roof than at home.

We also had a tiny red tent which we used for

hiking along the South Coastal Path down in Cornwall one year. I really wasn't too sure about that one at first, because I'm not a sardine and I sure felt like one when I was lying in it next to my mum and dad. But it was easier to carry for them in their rucksacks, so I had to make do.

We walked for miles and miles that holiday, and afterwards I dictated a picture story to my mum by getting her to put words to all the photos we had taken along the way, so Uncle Richard and Auntie Marina could share the experience and see all the places we had been to.

It was a lovely trip, even though we got lost at one stage and couldn't find the next campsite for what seemed like hours. And things got a bit fraught when we got trapped among a herd of cows. I would have shown them who's boss and herded them right off the meadow, but unfortunately my parents didn't let me.

That year was also the first time I got to go on a boat. Can't say I liked it much, even though I got to sit on my mum's lap, but Mummy and Papá did, so it was a case of grin and bear it. Make that just bear it. Truth be told, I could not wait to get off the stupid thing. Never got used to boats really. They're eerie.

There was a woman on the boat, who felt the exact same way I did. She clung to my mum for dear life, even though she didn't know her at all. Before you ask – yes, I let her. Felt almost as sorry for her as

I felt for myself.

Afterwards we continued walking along the coastline. We walked and walked and walked. And then we walked some more. And that's when I finally had enough. I remember Mummy and Papá asking me if I wanted to come along for yet another stroll in the evening, and that's when I went on strike and refused point blank to leave the tent. Even bared my teeth at them just to make sure they got it.

Guess what, the next day we walked some more. But it was the last holiday when I was still completely healthy, so I treasure the memory of it.

Chapter 7

THINGS I HATE

I wouldn't say I hated too many things. It was more a case of knowing exactly what I liked and what I didn't. Well, ok, apart from fireworks and exploding pellets that some stupid kids used to throw on the street outside our house. They always made me shiver in fear and no amount of *mimos* or reassurance from my parents would snap me out of it. The same goes for gunshots or unexpected loud bangs. Hate them, hate them, HATE THEM! If I heard any during my walks, I used to run straight back home. And Mummy and Papá would run straight after me. Because they wanted to catch me. Not because they were afraid, too.

I hated to be separated from my mum and dad. Either one of them. Which is why I want to come home so badly now. After all we were together almost all the time. I always made sure they were where they were supposed to be. I even visited them when they were sitting on the loo. Just pushed the door open and sidled up for yet another cuddle. Once I did the same to a lady who was just visiting. Just to get her used to the house rules. You should have seen her face!

I also hated postmen. My parents used to say that on the whole I was a rather unusual representative of my species, but when it came to my dislike of postmen, I was true dog. I LOATHED those guys with a vengeance and simply could not believe that they would dare to put their filthy post through the metal slot in my front door on a daily basis. I used to lie in wait each day by the window until I spied them park outside our house.

I then would jump off the sofa in a hurry and race down the stairs at break neck speed right up to the door, making damn sure I got there first. Then, just as the letter box was ever so slowly opened, because whoever was on the other side was hoping against hope that I wasn't there yet, would jump up and catch whatever they tried to push through the slot with my teeth, before they had the chance to let go, and pull with all my might and then tear it to shreds, just to show them who was boss. Apart from the annoyance, it was great fun, too.

One time my dad had ordered a book. Now, I didn't know that, otherwise I wouldn't have done what I did when it arrived by post. Or maybe I would. We will never know. In any case, since I didn't know, I simply saw red and chomped down on the offending item with all my might, ripping it right out of our postman's incoming hand. I heard my mum say later that the book looked as if it had been used by a vampire with teething problems, as in my anger I had punched my teeth straight through to page 88.

After that incident, my parents made sure to race past me down the stairs whenever they expected important post. And they also warned friends and family about my habit, in order to protect countless Christmas and birthday cards and especially important paperwork and cheques and the like from my almighty wrath.

Many years later, when I only had three legs and couldn't run down the stairs anymore, my parents almost came to miss our daily post routine. Almost. Funny, how life is, don't you think?!

Then there was this big Alsatian that I used to love to hate. He hated me right back, and his mum and my parents used to cross the road to try to avoid us seeing each other. Didn't always work as my sixth sense is quite developed, and then all hell would break loose as the two of us hurled insults at each other at the top of our voices across the street.

I never really cared that he was roughly five times my size, as I'm sure I would have won the fight. My parents, however, still count themselves lucky that they never got to find out what would have happened if we had met without our leads on.

Did I mention, that I don't like crowds? Well, I didn't. I always tried to avoid throngs of people in one place like the plague. Just stopped walking as soon as I spotted them and point blank refused to go down any crowded streets. And no amount of coercing, pleading or plain pulling on my lead would persuade me to move another inch. Simply sat right down and pulled a face. Made my parents laugh though, because apparently I have a very expressive face.

Towards the end of my life, my parents got around the problem by putting me in a pram.

Devious or what?! Let me tell you, I was not amused! Always wore a face of thunder as I was pushed through the crowds.

Oh, I almost forgot, I REALLY didn't like the vacuum cleaner. AT ALL! Nasty, sneaky things, vacuum cleaners. They just glide along, this way and that way, forwards and backwards, and always pull a person along with them. And then they take away all the nice smells, so you have to spend hours rubbing your scent back into the rugs and all over the furniture. They're dangerous, too! My friend Hamish once got his tongue stuck in one because the vacuum cleaner had sucked it right out of his barking mouth. Had to go to the vet to get it unstuck. Frightened him almost to death. Didn't frighten me though. I just bit it right where it hurt, every time it came along.

And I did the same to Auntie Marina's Ewbank. Uncle Richard thought it was terribly funny, so he filmed me doing it. And sometimes, when my aunt and uncle are sad that I'm not around anymore, they watch it together to cheer themselves up.

Another thing I won't miss are the ghosts in my house, which is ironic, because now I can see them clearly over here, they don't frighten me anymore. Probably because some would say that I'm also a ghost now. Especially my Auntie Barbara would say so, because I pushed my teeth against her leg once when she came round a few weeks ago and dared to empty the bin in our living room while my parents were away on holiday.

It frightened her because she really felt it, even though she couldn't see me. But then she should have known the rule about everything being mine once it hits the floor. Contents of bins included, in case you were wondering.

Auntie Barbara also heard me bark once when she knocked on the front door just after I had died. Had to let her know that things hadn't changed around here, just because I wasn't visible anymore.

Chapter 8

HAPPY DAYS

They say time flies when you're having fun, and it sure did.

Whatever was new in the beginning soon became one of my many routines.

Each morning my dad would get up really early and go downstairs to work, while my mum and I slept on for a little while longer.

And no, I didn't sleep in my parents' bed all night long. By choice, not because I wasn't allowed to. At first I really tried to, but truth be told, my parents wriggle about an awful lot during the night, and I really didn't fancy being accidentally kicked in the face or squashed.

So I would always start out each night in the middle of their bed, cosily tucked in between them.

But as soon as the lights went out and the snoring began, I would get out of there as fast as I could, before the flailing of arms and legs could start.

Damn nuisance, I tell you! I really would have preferred to stay.

Anyway, as soon as Mummy was awake in the morning, she would call out to Papá, and then he would bring her up a cup of tea and a treat for me. If she didn't wake up in time and I deemed that we had slept enough, I would wake her up by making this mewling sound at the back of my throat that my mum simply found irresistible. My mum calling out to Papá was also my signal to jump up onto their bed for the first extensive *mimo* session of the day.

My mum used to nuzzle me and then bury her face in my fur and inhale deeply. Like I said, she simply loved my smell and could never get enough of it.

I loved when she did that, but on the odd occasion she got carried away and overdid it, and then I had to growl or bare my teeth to make her stop.

As soon as Papá appeared she used to say, '*Barbita*!' (little beard). This was my signal to lick my dad's chin with his early morning stubble. He wasn't always too keen on it, but I didn't really care.

I also knew that if I was fast enough, I could get at his nose and ears at the same time. But I had to do it at the speed of lightning before he could push me off.

Another routine were our daily outings. I had different walks that I varied each day. I'm saying *I* and I mean *I*. Of course at first my parents decided where we would go (and I let them), but it didn't take long before I took over and made the decisions as to where we would go. I like to be in control. Always.

One of my favourite walks was to go down to the Fishermen's beach and meet up with the dogs down there. They were very different from the other dogs that I met on my walks. For starters they never had to put up with a lead, and there was just something about their demeanour that commanded respect. They somehow seemed to be in charge and I really wanted to be like them.

I also really liked our walks through the Country Park. Any of them. But especially the long one, the one that ended up with us going to the café on the hill. They allow dogs inside there. And they have carpets, which are great for rubbing off all the mud one has acquired whilst jumping into muddy puddles on the way there. My mum always used to say that I wasn't so different from a human toddler when it came to puddles. Always jumped right in.

At the café, Mummy and Papá almost always had a bite to eat before we walked back home. And that meant lots of yummy handouts under the table for me.

During my first spring I learned that people down here in Hastings, where I lived, like to dress up in funny costumes and paint their faces and hair all sorts of funny colours for festivals. They wrap themselves in ivy and other plants and flowers, and some of them put horns on their heads like rams, which is weird, because they don't do it at any other time. They also bang on drums quite a lot outside my window, which is a right nuisance when you're trying to snooze.

Summer came around and I discovered that people also like bathing in ponds and the sea like me. Only when *they* go in they make way more noise than I do. I also learned that people dress up in costumes for carnival and Pirate's Day. And drum some more.

Summer merged into autumn, and yes, you've guessed it, there was more dressing up to be done. And of course more drumming and carrying on. This time people even lit a huge bonfire on the beach and carried burning torches through the streets.

Unfortunately there were also very loud explosions and the evening ended with fireworks. I only saw them once and they freaked me out so much that my parents never took me on parades again. From that moment on, I spent festival nights either under the chair in Papá's studio or downstairs in the toilet. Always felt lousy, couldn't stop shaking like a leaf and never ever got used to them.

And then it was winter and it rained and rained and rained. I saw my very first Christmas tree, although I didn't really understand why people go to so much trouble to put lights and all that other stuff onto a tree. Didn't make much sense to me then and doesn't really now. But I guess, it was one of those things that marked the end of the year, and I always knew then that it would not be long now before spring would come back once more.

And so the years went around and around, from one routine to the next, until one year, just before the Christmas tree made a reappearance, something strange happened. White stuff started falling from the sky. I could see it from my vantage point on the sofa. Didn't recognise it and it sure didn't look like rain to me.

My mum started to sing this funny little song which I now know she always sings when it snows. And she seemed really happy. A few hours later, I couldn't believe what I was seeing from my window. The whole world had turned white. And then my parents finally put my parka on me and took me outside and shouted, 'Look, Nellie! Snow!'

Wow! It was magic! The white stuff was freezing cold and clung to my paws, but boy, was it fun to roll around in it! I couldn't get enough of it.

After a while we all went up the hill and there was even more of the stuff. Mountains of it. I had to hop from snowdrift to snowdrift like a rabbit. And then Papá made a ball from the snow and slowly rolled it around and around on the ground until it was one giant snowball. It was even bigger than myself. And then Mummy lifted me on top of it and took a picture as I was balancing on the snowball next to Papá.

Unfortunately, I also got the first major fright of my life not long after that. I think it was because everything looked so different in white and I got rather carried away, chasing snowflakes across the hill.

The last thing I remember is smelling rabbits under the hedges and wondering where they were hiding, and chasing after them. Then all of a sudden I was completely lost. Luckily I had stopped running by then, as unbeknownst to me I had reached the edge of the hill. I almost fell off the cliff.

I could never tell my parents how close I came to dying that day, but I think somehow they knew.

I could hear my mum crying and screaming my name at the top of her voice somewhere in the distance, whilst I was slowly clawing my way back from the edge. And I know my dad threw off his big winter coat and his jumper and crawled in only his T-shirt through the snow and into the undergrowth, in his haste to get to me. He got mightily scratched by the brambles, but he just didn't care, he was so happy to see me emerge on shaky legs from the bushes.

That was the first time my mum cried over me and I have never forgotten that day.

Because most of the people I love speak different languages, I got to learn them too. My parents would start by speaking English to me and then switch to Spanish or German or French, or even to spelling words, if they didn't want me to get the meaning. Unfortunately for them I am a very fast learner.

I even learned to spell. Especially words like 'walk' or 'W. A. L. K.' never got past me. From the very beginning I always knew what the letters meant. My parents never figured out how I was able to do it. The same went for 'Sh...', as in 'Shall we go for a walk?' Hearing that always woke me right up, and I immediately got up to go before my parents could even finish the sentence.

In the mornings I sometimes practised to speak like them. I never got it 100 percent right, but my mum swears that on one occasion it sounded like 'Mama'.

Some of the words I liked better than others. For

example I hated the word *ciao*, because it always meant that someone was leaving, but I loved 'let's go' because it meant I could come along, too.

Sometimes my parents also invented words, but I got their meaning soon enough. One of those words was *quicklypipino*. That was our own word for my last pee of the day. It was the time of night I got to hang out with my dad, just before bedtime. He would very slowly ask me: 'Would... you... like... to... go... for... a... *quicklypipino*?'

I would cock my head at the first 'W', and as soon as he finished the sentence, I would jump off the sofa and run so fast towards the door, my claws would scratch off the floor paint. If you don't believe me, go to my house – you can still see the scratch marks all over the floorboards.

And then my dad and I would wander around the block until I had finished my business. Night after night, come rain or shine. Some nights I would hold it all in for as long as I could, just to hang out a bit longer with my dad.

My parents and I even had a secret sign language for things I wanted. Some signs my parents came up with, but I also invented a few of them myself.

For example, each time I wanted to be covered by a blanket in my bed, I used to scratch my sheet and then look up to see if my parents got the drift. If they didn't, I would scratch some more. And then some more. Until they did.

It was originally my mum who had started to cover me with a blanket before going to sleep, but in the end she and Papá had to take turns to do so, because I had gotten used to it so much that I would wake them up several times during the night demanding to be covered.

It was only quite a few years later, when my mum invented a system of hooking my blanket under the feet of my bed so that I wasn't able to inadvertently throw it off anymore, that my parents got to sleep through the night again.

Another routine I liked, was going places. We used to do it at various times of the year. I never realised just how big the world is. It goes on forever and ever. It took ages to get to the end of it by car. There were endless valleys and mountains and creeks to explore. And big standing stones and caves (where I was told off for peeing), and long beaches with sand or pebbles (where I wasn't). We went mostly alone and sometimes with Auntie Dee and Uncle Vini. We even went a few times with Auntie Pachy and Grandma Olga.

We almost always ended up sleeping in a caravan. Or a tent. Or some strange hotel room on the odd occasion, where I refused to be left behind when they wanted to go out for a meal, because I was scared.

Sleeping in a hotel room together with Auntie Pachy and Grandma Olga was fun. Kind of. Until Grandma Olga started to snore and make other noises. Then none of us slept so well. Only her.

Back at home a few things changed over the years. The windows were rotten, so new ones got put in and I supervised. Papá's studio got too small for him, so Mummy decided to move us out of the master bedroom and into his former studio to sleep. She figured, if we could sleep well together in a tent, we could manage in a tiny room, too.

So our former bedroom became Papá's new studio. Again I supervised, as she was painting and redecorating both. I didn't mind the changes, as I still had access to my bed, my parent's bed and to the window. Also, it was cosier all in all, as we were closer together.

The last thing that changed, just a few months before I died, was our bathroom. My parents saved up for that one. It took ages to complete, but was well worth it in the end. Even though we were covered in dust for about two months flat.

Chapter 9

CHANGES

But all good things must come to an end, and so the good times we had, did too.

Last night I heard my parents talking. They were saying that it's funny how you remember mostly the sad and upsetting things that happen in such stark detail, whereas the good times just seem to roll by unnoticed and are taken for granted. And that you only really notice them when they are gone.

But we had so many good years together and I have so many happy memories, that I can wrap them around myself like my favourite white blanket. The one with the holes in it. From my teeth. It's still there in our bedroom, draped across my bed, and when I close my eyes I can almost feel it covering me, like it used to.

It started very slowly, almost unnoticeably. A little twinge in my right shoulder at first, then a slight limp, then I was back to normal again and we all forgot about it.

My mum looked it up in her diaries the other day. That's how she found out that we had seven good years together before things started to change. But slowly, ever so slowly, so we wouldn't notice.

The whole thing really began with a fatty lump on my flank. I had it for years and it was tiny at first, but as it slowly grew bigger and bigger, my parents and the vet finally decided it was time to get rid of it. I was almost eight years old and it was late spring, and I was really, really scared. The vet put a needle into my bottom, whilst I sat shivering on my mum's lap, and then everything went kind of fuzzy.

The next thing I remember is waking up, and being really confused because my parents were not where they had been before, and instead of my mum's lap, I was in a cage that I didn't remember getting into. I thought for an awful moment that I was back at the kennel of the rescue centre, and I was so scared I started to howl at the top of my voice. Luckily my parents had anticipated this happening and were waiting just outside. I remember racing up to them as soon as the kennel door was opened, but falling over because someone had put me in a baby grow, even though I am not a baby. And then my mum caught me and picked me up, like she always did when I was frightened and really needed her. And she kissed me a lot and held me, and Papá did the same.

But all I wanted to do was to race back to the car, where I knew I would be safe from the vet. We all got home safely that day and when my parents finally got the results back from the vet's, they were told that the lump had just been fat and nothing to worry about.

My mum told Auntie Dee years later that the whole episode had felt like a lucky escape for us all, but that deep down something had started to change and like so often in life we didn't even realise it.

For my part, it took me ages to get over the experience. I couldn't stop myself from whining and crying non-stop for a few days because I was so stressed. I even peed myself twice and I NEVER pee myself.

You see, I simply couldn't understand what had happened. I kept trying to figure it out, but nothing made sense. Mummy says it's because I was too intelligent for my own good, and that I had somehow figured out that I had lost a bit of time, during which something scary had happened.

Now of course I know what happened, but back then I kept dwelling on the fact that I had been sitting on my mum's lap one moment and then been somewhere else entirely the next. With a very painful bald patch on my side and bits of thread hanging out that I wasn't allowed to chew off. Oh, and I had to wear the baby grow all the time until the vet pulled the stitches out. Of course it was better than a protective collar, but not by much.

After that, things went back to normal for a while and we got on with our lives.

But later that year, I started to get painful boil-like sores on my paw, right between my toes. When they didn't go away after a while, my parents took me to the vet and I was given antibiotics. Unfortunately that didn't help and so my sores became worse.

At first my mum thought it might be a grass

allergy and the vet wondered if there was possibly something wrong with my *moon system* (weird, I know – I didn't know I had one in the first place). But we never found out for sure.

Years later my parents found out that a lot of dogs, who were walked on or near the beach, came out with the same sores, and that someone had sprayed poison to kill the weeds in the area. So the most likely culprit for my sores would be that.

That, or what my parents call *pollution*. I heard them talk about it a lot, but the whole thing never made much sense to me. I mean, why don't people like grass and plants to grow naturally so that you can eat them (or pee on them) without getting sores and stomach cramps afterwards? And why do they blow all that stinky stuff into the air so it hurts to breathe?

Where we live, right by the sea, it should be nice and clean and smell of salt and fish. But it doesn't. Most of the times it burns the insides of my nose because of all the grey stuff that come out of the back of cars and the tops of chimneys. And in winter you can barely breathe because of all the wood fires.

My mum used to walk around with a scarf over her face at times because she didn't want to breathe it all in. Unfortunately I couldn't do the same. She tried telling someone official about it, but they didn't want to listen. Not even when my parents had their blood tested (yuck, why would you?!) and got a letter back saying *abnormal carbon monoxide levels*. I'm not exactly sure what that means, but I think it's what all the smoke does to your insides. They didn't test me, but my parents were pretty sure I had it as well.

Anyway, what followed were four long years of sores on my paws. They came, they went, they moved from one toe to the next, from front paw to back paw and back again. They looked like angry red mounds and chafed like mad. I was in agony, and during all this time my parents never once gave up trying to find a solution.

My mum researched everywhere and everything she could think of. She also spent hours talking to Auntie Pachy on the phone because my aunt knows a lot about plants and herbs and remedies.

She even bought boots for me to wear. Not only did I look absolutely ridiculous in them, but after a few wobbly steps I also nearly fell over. And that was the end of that.

She spent hours and hours reading up on things and talking to people in her search for an answer and a cure. My mum is like that. She needs to know why something is happening and will always try to fix it.

Did I tell you that we once had a butterfly called Fairdinand, who lived with us for a while? Yep, Mummy found him inside a box of melons in a shop during a freezing cold winter some years back, and just had to rescue him from certain death.

I remember her carrying him safely inside her cupped hands to the car, where my dad and I were waiting, and we then drove home with him.

After that, my mum spent quite some time trying to find out what butterflies eat, and how to get Fairdinand through the winter. He lived mainly downstairs, where she put slices of oranges, honey and sugar water down for him to eat and drink, which I wasn't allowed to touch.

But sometimes he used to fly up the stairs and visit us in the living room. He lived quite a long time with us, but sadly didn't make it until spring, because a spider got him, which upset my mum a lot.

She kept thinking, if only he had lived another week, he would have been safe. Because one week later the sun came out and it would have been warm enough for Fairdinand to be released back into the wild.

But such is life. And my mum hates that bit about life a lot.

As it happened, we had a lovely walk up to the Country Park, and while I was running around, happy to be out and about, my parents carried Fairdinand's tiny body to his final resting place among the grass and the early spring flowers.

Unfortunately my sores also resisted a multitude of ointments and treatments. I lost count of how many things were rubbed, dropped or dabbed onto them. Most of the stuff I ate because I hate sticky toes. That's when my mum put socks on me. Undignified to say the least! Of course, as soon as she left the room, I had them off. So the socks were replaced by bandages, held in place by sticky tape. They didn't fare much better than the socks where I was concerned.

I figured: my paws, my sores, MY treatment. That is: mainly licking and chewing, especially after the vet had cut into them to see what was under the swelling. Nothing as it turned out.

For a while my sores got better when doused in some blue liquid, called *Agua De Alibour,* which my mum had shipped over from Argentina. When that stopped working, I got homoeopathic remedies added to my food, which made everything taste yucky and didn't exactly improve my mood or my patience. In the end, my mum opted for washing my feet in camomile tea and warm water, with a few drops of a herbal antiseptic tincture added to it EVERY time I went for a walk.

Considering that I left the house two to four times each day and she did this until the day I died, we're talking a lot of footbaths! Fine by me, as it seemed to help, and I could always do with the extra cuddles.

And then, about eight months before my death, the sores all of a sudden miraculously disappeared, never to come back again.

Maybe the foot baths helped, or maybe the sores knew that I was going to die soon and therefore simply couldn't be bothered to come back.

Other than the paw trouble, life went on as usual. My parents worked a lot, and then we went on holiday again to Cornwall. This time it rained pretty much non-stop, which wasn't fun because we all got cold and wet in our tent.

At the end of that year, Uncle Richard decided to add Christmas dinners to my annual birthday dinners and I ended up eating tons of steak, especially since Auntie Marina didn't really want to eat hers and secretly fed it to me under the table.

I always wore a black bow tie for the occasion. NOT my choice at all, but I decided to turn a blind eye, since it meant more food coming my way. And I was a real foodie, as my parents put it. That's why they knew right at the end that something was seriously wrong with me when I stopped eating. Because I always ate. Even when I was very poorly.

Two years before I died, Uncle Vini and Auntie Dee sold their flat in London, and because they didn't have a new place to stay yet, they moved in with us. They only stayed three months, but I couldn't have been happier. For two reasons. Number one, I was always a bit scared in their old flat, because Grandma Olga and I heard ghostly sounds in there on more than one occasion and I never felt 100 percent safe after that. And number two, it was just *soooo* nice to have most of the people I love under one roof together where I could keep an eye on them.

Even my Auntie Pachy came over for a visit. It was the last time I ever saw her, only we didn't know it at the time.

When spring came that year, I started to limp. Something just didn't feel right with my left hind leg, so I stopped using it for a while. Because I was always running around and playing like mad, everyone thought I had pulled a muscle or something and the vet gave me painkillers. But they only made me vomit and gave me a bad case of diarrhoea. Mummy quickly had to carry me outside and across the road in her pyjamas in the middle of the night because we don't have a garden, and we only just made it in time.

So back to the vet for me, which wasn't fun. Not for the vet and definitely not for me.

This time he thought that I had possibly torn a ligament in my knee, and after another lot of different painkillers, the vet decided to operate. Only when I was out for the count, did he change his mind at the very last moment, as my X-rays apparently didn't show clearly enough if I had a problem with my ligament or not.

I'm just telling you what I heard, because for most of this I was either unconscious or in too much pain to care. Also, the new painkillers made me super drowsy and all I wanted to do was to sleep.

Finally our vet referred me to another vet, about an hour and a half's drive away from us, who was a specialist in muscles and bones. This one was very friendly and I would have really liked him if he hadn't been a vet. As it was, I tried to do my usual best to resist any examination. Luckily for him I was very weak by then, after yet another bad night of vomiting and diarrhoea. So in the end I decided to just let him get on with it.

I was X-rayed for the second time, but the vet said that no visible damage to my ligaments could be seen or felt, apart from a swollen area around my knee. He therefore sent me home with antibiotics and some other pills, which I didn't mind because my parents hid them in my favourite meatballs.

I got to eat quite a lot of them over the coming months. Of course I also figured out over time how to eat the meatballs without the pills – I'm not stupid after all. And spitting the pills to one side only meant more meatballs in the end, as my parents had to make sure I swallowed all of my medicine.

While all this went on and I wasn't getting much better despite my meds, my mum, in her search for a cure, spoke to Auntie Pachy on the phone, who then asked her vet in Buenos Aires what he would do. This one told her to use antibiotics against both, *aerobic* and *anaerobic bacteria* (whatever that means) and after a consultation with the nice vet back home, they decided to give it a try. The swelling went down, but my pain remained, and by now I was so poorly that I had to go back to the vet's to have yet more X-rays. And that's when he found a swelling in my right shoulder.

Yep, my right shoulder. Not the left hind leg I wasn't using. Funny how life is. I could have told them it hurt in there, but nobody spoke enough dog to be able to understand what I was saying.

So the vet told my parents he needed to do a biopsy. Can't tell you much about it, because I was asleep when he did it. When the results came back, he told my parents that there was nothing wrong with my left leg, but that there was a chance that I had cancer in my right shoulder.

But you see, because I was limping with my left hind leg and because the vet said the results were not conclusive, nobody believed him. Not my mum, not my dad, nor any of my aunts and uncles. They all thought I had a swelling in my right shoulder because I had strained it by putting all my weight on it, in my effort not to use my left hind leg.

At this stage the vet suggested to send me somewhere else, where I could have a CT or MRI scan. I didn't have a clue what that meant, but that's what he said.

My parents were very upset that nobody had been able to help me so far, and that's when they remembered the vet from the telly. You know, the one who makes animals better by doing complicated operations and by giving them shiny new limbs if they can't use their own anymore. I had seen him on the telly, too, and he seemed nice enough, even though he was a vet.

So my parents asked and we finally got permission to go and see him. Only we didn't get to see him personally in the end, because they sent us to his other hospital, the one that deals with cancer.

At first Mummy and Papá were annoyed at that because they still didn't believe I had cancer. But they didn't have a choice, and later that spring they took me there.

I don't like to remember it much because my mum and dad had to leave me there for the examination and the scan. I barked and howled for hours and had to wear a muzzle because I wouldn't let anyone touch me. It was so horrible, I even used my hind leg again in my hurry to get away from it all.

Then, a few days later, the results came back. They still called them inconclusive, but the new vet also suspected a tumour in my right shoulder. And he was an expert in everything cancer. My mum and dad cried when they heard that, but then they clung on to the fact that the results were not conclusive and took the vet up on his offer to watch me for a while, to see what would happen.

And that's when Mummy seriously got going. From herbal remedies to tinctures, from lotions to potions to daily shoulder massages, I had it all.

She also started to do some serious research into arthritis, because it was thought that that had possibly caused me to limp in the first place.

This is what my mum wrote to the vet two months later:

'With *regards to his left hind leg, the one with the suspected arthritis, Nelson is going from strength to strength. After we last spoke and Nelson had finished his course of pain medication, we did a bit of research into which herbal remedies could possibly help him with the arthritis and his ligaments, muscles and health in general.*

We started him off on plant-based antioxidants, flaxseed oil (omega 3,6 and 9) and turmeric powder. To our surprise Nelson almost immediately got better and slowly started to use his hind leg again.

I then read about a clinical trial at the University of Montreal in 2014, where they tried a number of herbal remedies on dogs with arthritis with great success. Unfortunately, whatever they used is not available to buy yet, but having found out which plant-based remedies had been used in the trial, we started giving Nelson glucosamine, chondroitin, MSM, white willow bark, glutamine, turmeric, bromelain, ginger, blackcurrant leaf extract, and devil's claw as well as the plant-based antioxidants and the flaxseed oil.

Now obviously this is only anecdotal evidence and maybe it is just coincidence, but Nelson is doing amazingly fine.

He uses his leg all the time now, has started to run and climb stairs again and his leg muscles are getting stronger all the time. I've attached two short videos for you to see.

As you can see, he really is happy in himself and

we're so glad that he's enjoying life to the full once more!

So now it's fingers firmly crossed that he continues this way and it wasn't just a lucky blip.'

Famous last words…

I had a happy late spring and early summer with picnics and lots of walks. But even though my parents didn't notice, deep down I felt the pain and I just knew that something wasn't right anymore. Mummy says I became even more selective with who could touch me, and she was the only one who was allowed to carry me around and up and down our stairs.

Only a few weeks after my mum had written to the vet, the pain in my shoulder got so bad that I started to limp again. Only this time with my right front leg. The one with the suspected tumour in my shoulder. If it had stayed that way, my parents would have taken me straight back to the vet's, but after taking a few painkillers I felt better again.

July turned into August and I started to limp on and off and couldn't walk very far. My parents still thought it was a strain or sprain, or possibly a muscle tear, and so they bought me a pram to take me places.

A pram, I kid you not! At first I was mortified, but then I quite liked it because now I was higher up and could look down on all the other dogs. It also meant I could go everywhere again.

My parents however got funny looks, and on more than one occasion my mum got the impression that people thought she put me in a pram because she didn't have human children and wanted to play mother. It earned her a few nasty looks, too, because people thought she was using me as a doll and didn't want to let me walk. She certainly did a lot of explaining during that time.

In September of that year we went away to Devon on holiday. At first it was great, even though I was silently in a lot of pain. I tried my best not to show it though. It was also the first and last time I went kayaking with my parents. They hired a doggie swim vest for me and off we went. Scary stuff, the sea! I definitely enjoyed coming back from that little trip. But the swim vest was great. When I figured out that it helped me to swim, I paddled right around the boat. Loved it so much that my parents bought it for me. Little did they know that I would never use it again.

At the end of our holidays our car got stuck in mud and wouldn't drive anymore. So my parents had to have it – and us – picked up by a huge truck. Halfway home at a motorway station, we had to change trucks. I got to sit next to Mummy and Papá each time. Right behind the driver.

Can't say that I liked him much, so every time he started to speak, I would just growl and bark to shut him up. Worked wonders. He didn't say much after that for the rest of the almost eight-hour journey. We were more exhausted than at the start of our holidays, when we finally arrived back home.

Autumn went by and nothing much happened. Then, just before my parents put up the Christmas tree once more, I couldn't hide my pain any longer, and no amount of pain killers and being driven around in a pram made it any better.

In the end Mummy called the last vet again. And she sent him videos of me to show him how I was limping. As a result we were told to come at once and see him again. I really didn't want to, but I had no choice.

We saw the New Year in with loads of scary

fireworks and a few days later my parents took me back to the vet's. I was so scared that I pooed myself as soon as I saw him coming into the room. The vet was quite shocked and more than a little offended because he hadn't even touched me yet. Needless to say, I had to have another scan. Don't remember much as they knocked me out for it.

Afterwards my parents were there to pick me up and we stayed overnight in a hotel nearby. When they went for a meal, they took me with them. I was really groggy from the anaesthetics. All I remember is peeing inside the restaurant and that we all pretended that it hadn't happened.

This time the scan was conclusive. And it screamed CANCER. My mum almost screamed too. And then she cried. And cried. And cried some more. My dad cried, too. Only a bit less, because he was trying to be strong for Mummy's sake. But I know that he was hurting. And so was I. An awful lot.

The vet explained that bone pain is the most severe pain you can have and that it can't be suppressed by pain killers. I could have told him that. And then he suggested I have an amputation. He also told my parents that this would be quite a routine operation and that, since I wasn't really using my right front leg anymore anyway, it wouldn't make much of a difference to me. In fact, it would make things easier as I would almost immediately be out of pain.

When my mum looked up the details *on the line,* which pretty much confirmed what the vet had said, she found that someone had written that 'dogs have three legs and a spare' and that there was even a so-called *Tripawd* community out there.

It gave my mum and dad hope, and luckily I didn't know what was to come. But quite frankly, even if I had, I doubt I would have cared. Anything was better than the constant pain.

I remember my parents having a quick chat because they were running out of money fast, with the all the costs for my vet appointments and scans and all my medicines mounting up. The irony was that they had cancelled my insurance only two months or so before my troubles started because it cost too much each month. Had they known what was to come, they wouldn't have done that, I can tell you. My vet bills ran into the thousands, and my parents once calculated that the only single thing they ever paid more for, was our house.

So, to be able to let me have my operation they had to take out a loan that day. They are still paying it off, by the way, and will be doing so for a few more years to come, even though I'm not there anymore.

And so, three days later, I had my amputation. The funny thing was, the vet was right. As soon as they asked me, 'Where are your Mummy and Daddy?' I ran over to them. On three legs. Without falling over.

I was bloody and bruised and my mum said I looked like Frankenstein's dog – whoever that was. I had no hair around my shoulder and tummy and massive scars all over the place because the vet had not only removed my leg, but also extracted another fatty lump on my ankle and a wart on my belly.

Luckily no cancer was found anywhere else apart from inside the shoulder joint, which had been removed along with my leg.

And that's how the story should have ended. With a 'And then they lived happily ever after; it was tough for a while, but everything worked out in the end'. But of course that's not what happened, because sometimes life isn't like that.

My hair slowly grew back, the massive bruises were fading and my scars were healing, even though Mummy thought she could have done a better job sewing me together, as I had a pouch-like bit of skin dangling over the stitches.

I could walk and run and pick a fight with

bigger dogs from day one, but my mood was another matter. I was very depressed and scared and couldn't bark for a while without howling with pain. I only snapped out of it when Mummy carried me over to Auntie Marina's, a week or so after my operation. I guess it reminded me that everything around me still was exactly the same as before.

The staircases in our house are quite steep and slippery, so my mum had to start carrying me up and down the stairs. Since, OF COURSE, she was required to ask for my permission to do so, she came up with a new signal. She would sit down next to me on the top step and count to three, at which point she would slap her thigh to invite me to step on it, so she could pick me up and carry me. And so I would. Or not, as the case may be.

I didn't let anyone else do this, only occasionally my dad, when my mum wasn't available because, as I have said before, I have my pride.

Also, I never quite forgave my dad for letting the vet steal my leg without defending me. This was partly my misunderstanding of what had happened and partly the nurse's fault, because she turned around to face my parents when I was sedated but conscious in her arms and couldn't move a muscle to run away. My mum had already left the room after handing my groggy self over to the nurse, and so the last thing I saw before they operated on me, was my dad leaving without me. Which is why I tried to nip him whenever he tried to pick me up after that. He really missed my cuddles a lot, and I am very sorry I didn't understand that he only tried to save me.

Chapter 10

ENDINGS

This is the chapter that I like the least, because it's all about saying goodbye and I really don't want to think about it. But I guess you need to know what happened, so I'm going to tell you anyway.

The last year of my life started out on a positive note. Everyone thought that I had finally rounded the corner and overcome all my problems. My parents were intensely proud of me, as I was almost as mobile on three legs as I had been on four.

My dad taught me once to never give up and so to everyone's utter amazement I even managed to pee balancing on two legs whilst cocking the third, which was no mean feat.

Ok, so occasionally I smacked my face into the pavement, but that was only when I forgot that my leg had gone and put my missing foot down. To avoid any injuries to my face, my parents made me wear an inflatable ring as a cushion around my neck for a while, but I soon didn't need it anymore.

On the whole I felt so much better. I went for walks again, I visited my favourite creeks and puddles in the woods once more, I ran along the beach chasing pebbles, and I dug holes with one front leg. It didn't slow my digging speed down at all, which surprised my parents no end. Sometimes I would use my missing front leg to dig and surprise myself because the hole I was digging didn't get any deeper.

And if I got tired at any time and wanted a lift, I would simply sidle up to my mum and touch her leg. She would then ask me: *'A upa?'* (which is Spanish baby speak for 'Do you want to be lifted up?'), and if I pressed her leg in agreement, she would say *'Poppi!'* which is one of her made up words, that would tell me to curl my bottom under to make it easier for her to pick me up. Told you I was good with languages!

Oh, and if I didn't want to be picked up after all, as I am prone to change my mind quite easily, I would simply back away and flash my teeth. Simple as that.

All was good, even though the sores on my paws made two short last appearances. But then they went, never to return again.

The only other scary thing were the ghosts that I started to see at nights sometime during spring that year. It got so bad that I refused to sleep in our bedroom and tried to hide behind the furniture in Papá's studio instead. But I could still see them everywhere. So my mum took to sleeping on the sofa with me for almost a month. It wasn't just me who saw the ghosts either. My friend Bindi across the road also couldn't sleep because of them and kept her mum awake all night long. Luckily all this stopped eventually and things went back to normal.

Then came summer. And what a hot summer it was! My parents decided to go on holiday to a caravan park not far away from us. We spent a week there in a caravan, and I got to explore everything, mainly from the safety of my pram, as my parents didn't want to tire me out. Also, they found that I was strangely reluctant to stray far from the caravan on foot.

We went to another holiday park near Hythe after that and stayed another week in yet another caravan. That was less nice, because I could hear shots being fired all the time on the army base in the distance and I didn't like it one bit.

Unbeknown to us that was my last holiday ever.

After that holiday things were a flurry of activities for my parents, as Papá had a festival to organise and run with the help of my mum. And then we had a new bathroom put in, and I took my frustration out on the plumber by barking at him on a daily basis for the two months or so it took him to finish his job. I only ever shut up when my parents were out and I was alone with him. Because in all honesty, I didn't dare do it to his face without backup. Just in case he would retaliate. This amused the plumber no end, and he even sent my parents a video as proof of how well I behaved when I was without them. The traitor!

Then Grandma C came over for a last visit – not that she knew that it was the last time she would ever see me. And that's the time when I bit her, if you remember.

After that not much happened. I got to shower in our new bathroom, and we went for walks and did the usual things. Christmas came and went and we spent New Year's Eve with Auntie Dee and Uncle Vini. I even got to dance with Auntie Dee to take my mind off the blasted fireworks.

The New Year started like they always do around here: cold, wet and miserable, which meant more footbaths for me. A short while later I started to sneeze. And sneeze. Couldn't stop. Really banged my head on the floor a few times.

And then just as spring was starting out once more, I got this horrible cough. Always had to cough three times or so and then retch. And my eyes started to tear a lot. So the vet was called and he tested me for lung worms. Luckily I didn't have any, but my cough didn't get any better either. In fact it got worse.

And that's when my mum did her usual research *on the line*. She found out that what I had sounded awfully like kennel cough, and since the vet agreed, I was put on antibiotics once more. This time I did mind, despite the meatballs they were hidden in. That's when I perfected the art of eating the meatballs without my meds. But Mummy always noticed and one way or another she got the damn things down my throat anyway.

When I didn't get better, the vet told my mum that kennel cough is a virus that sometimes has a bacterial component for which antibiotics are given. But the viral bit of it just has to be endured until it runs its course. So in the meantime, my mum gave me herbal remedies to strengthen my *moon system,* and raw organic honey to soothe my throat and to help kill the bacteria. And when things got worse and I couldn't sleep for coughing, my dad used to fan the steam from a bowl of hot water into my face to give me inhalations.

Sadly I only got worse. And slowly the vet came round to the idea that despite the signature cough, maybe this wasn't kennel cough after all. As I got weaker and weaker, I didn't really feel like walking much anymore. My mum took to sleeping on the sofa next to me once more, but despite this I felt utterly lousy.

Another trip to the vet later, my parents, who always try to do things as natural as possible when it comes to medicines, finally agreed for me to be given something called *anti-inflammatory steroids.* They were worried about the side effects, but there wasn't really anything else left to try. And for a moment it seemed as if a miracle had finally happened: within four hours of me taking the pills, I was almost back to feeling normal. I felt so perky I jumped off the sofa for the first time in ages and fetched my favourite toy, which I then handed to my very surprised Auntie Dee. Because I felt all of a sudden very much like playing again.

I felt so good, I demanded to go for a walk right there and then. So off we went to the beach and I ran and fetched stones my dad threw for me. I even went for a long walk through the Country Park with my parents the next day and refused to be carried when I ran out of breath. Maybe deep down I knew that it was the last time I would ever walk there. My mum used to say that with steroids it's often a case of 'what goes up, must come down', and unfortunately that's exactly what happened with me. For exactly five days I felt happy and healthy again and savoured every moment of it until things came crashing down again.

On day six I started to feel out of breath and so I breathed faster and faster and louder and louder. My brother Oscar had died hyperventilating, so my parents recognised the signs. Mummy read somewhere that a dog breathes normally 10-35 times per minute. When she timed my breathing, she found that I had started to breathe between 51 and 60 times per minute instead.

It was Easter Sunday and my parents carried me to the beach one final time. We stayed all afternoon on an inflatable mattress under a parasol my dad had put up just for me, covered by my favourite blanket, looking out to sea. Only this time I didn't chase any dogs, nor did I demand my dad throw any stones for me to find like I always used to do. I just concentrated on breathing in and out, and then I tried to memorise every last little detail of everything. The smells, the wind on my face, the pebbles on my beach and Mummy and Papá at my side.

We even had a picnic that day, and I wanted to make my parents happy, so I forced myself to eat a little. Not much, but just enough to give them hope. And after that I never ate a bite again.

The next day, after a horrible night, my parents rushed me back for emergency X-rays at the vet's. But strangely by the time we got there, the X-ray machine had broken down mysteriously. So the vet sent us back home with some pills for me, to hopefully flush the fluid out of my lungs. Sadly they never worked and only made me pee non-stop. But thanks to the X-ray machine breaking down when it did, I got to stay one more day with my family, and we could say goodbye properly.

The day before I died, my dad had to go to London to work and Auntie Dee and Uncle Vini were not in town either. But my mum was. She sat with me the entire day, because deep down she knew that it was our last day together. I know, because I heard her tell my Auntie Pachy on the phone. And I guess I knew too, but I couldn't really think much, because I had to concentrate so very hard on breathing.

And boy, was I thirsty! So in the end Mummy stopped giving me my medicines and we just sat on the sofa together all day long and talked. Well, my mum talked and I listened. She reminded me of all the things we had done together, and all the wonderful times we had had together. She told me that she would always remember me, and that she loved me very much. Over and over and over again.

And then she sang to me, because it always made me feel better when she did that. She sang *My Favourite Things* and *Wenn Der Weiße Flieder Wieder Blüht,* and *You Keep Coming Back Like A Song*. But I could barely make out the words because she was crying so much, and that made my heart hurt as well as my lungs and my tummy.

I can still hear her singing now, because whenever I am near her these days, she sings the same songs she sang to me on our last day together. And whenever she suddenly hears those songs in her head, she knows I am there, because dead people come back to her in songs. Her grandpa and her grandma also have their own songs and Mummy hears them whenever they come over for a visit.

The other thing I remember about our last day together, is the fact that Mummy carried me across the road for a pee every two hours or so. And then she carried me back and held my head so that I could drink some water. She did it all day long and right through the night. She told Papá that she would have carried me to the end of the world if it would have made any difference. And I know that that's the truth.

She carried me a lot during the last year of my life – up the stairs, down the stairs, to the car and back again. And sometimes, when I got too tired during one of our walks, she carried me through the woods or along the shore. She carried me so much she slipped a disk in her neck because I was so heavy. But she didn't care because she loved me. And it sure was comfortable to be carried around.

Papá carried me too, but I didn't let him do it so often because I didn't want him to think that I was a baby. And I REALLY didn't like to be carried whenever there were other dogs around. I had to think of my reputation you know!

As I said, my mum had been the only one who stayed with me the day before I died. But in the evening Papá returned from working in London and I was mightily glad he did. My parents then carried me upstairs to their bedroom to have a last long look out of the window together. Because they knew deep down that it was going to be the last time. I guess I did too, but because I was concentrating so hard to breathe in and out, I was kind of distracted.

Anyway, there we were, the three of us, lying on the bed together, looking out to sea and creating one last beautiful memory together. And then my mum carried me downstairs to the living room and put me down on the sofa so that I was more comfortable. Papá slept upstairs and Mummy slept on a mattress on the floor across the room from me.

And that's how we spent our last night together.

On the day I died, my Auntie Dee and Uncle Vini came over one last time to say goodbye. My mum had told them the day before that it might be a good idea for them to come and see me, before I was going to the vet's in the morning. She told them that there was the tiniest chance everything would be ok, but that she didn't really believe it. She also told them that we were going to leave around 10:40am and that she would understand if they would not be able to make it, because they were only driving back from their trip to London that very morning.

But you know what, they just made it in time

with about five minutes to spare. I was so happy to see them, but I could barely wag my tail, and I tried so hard to sit up when I heard them arrive. We had a quiet last chat together and they told me that they loved me, and that it was okay to let go. And then my parents carried me to the car for my last journey ever.

On the way out of the house, Uncle Richard suddenly appeared out of nowhere. He hadn't realised that my time here was up and he thought I was going to be fine. Especially as I mustered one last bout of strength to bark and snap at him because, yes, you guessed it, he'd forgotten rule number one and touched my back. This was really my mum's fault because she made the mistake of telling him it would be okay to do so, seeing as I was so weak.

Boy, did that wake me up! I mean, rules are rules, never mind how dire the situation.

I did feel very guilty about it later on though because it left Uncle Richard with a bad last memory of me, and so I got my mum to write him a last goodbye and apology note on my behalf.

Anyway. I had one last pee by the road side and off

we went in our car.

Did I mention that I loved that car? It was practically my second home. Once I had overcome my original fears, I felt so safe inside. It carried me to all the exciting places I got to visit and back home again.

And I adored going parking with either of my parents. Papá used to come back home late sometimes from rehearsals or meetings, and then I would sit in the window and watch out for him. I always knew when he was about to come back home because Mummy's phone would ring, and that was my signal to push open the curtains with my nose and to wait until he arrived. He would drive past the house just for me and pick me up to go parking, up the road somewhere. And then we would walk back home together. It was the best thing ever!

I did the same with Mummy whenever she came back, especially from shopping on Mondays. Sometimes I liked being in the car so much that I would refuse to leave it. My mum then had to drag me out, snarling and snapping, which made us both very cross.

I remember that last day was the first time ever I forgot to be scared by the vet. I was in so much pain, I didn't really care anymore. Normally I would shake and shiver and hyperventilate on Mummy's lap each time we went there. But that last time was different. I just didn't have the energy to do it.

I heard the vet say to my parents that he was going to sedate me to x-ray my lungs. As I said, because I was feeling so lousy, I didn't really care anymore. I remember the prick of a needle and then everything went really hazy and fuzzy and heavy, and I don't remember much of what happened until I got here.

I only have vague bits of memory of the in-between. Like in a dream. Like snippets of sounds and pictures. My mum holding me and kissing me. My dad stroking me. Bits of their voices. Being carried outside into the back room. The vet bringing me back, saying something about my lungs being full of cancer. My parents crying. My mum nibbling my ear. My dad kissing my head. Somebody shaving my neck. Another little prick. And then everything went black.

And when I woke up, I was here. At first I didn't get at all what had happened. I kept barking at my parents, 'Let's go, let's go, I'm feeling so much better! What are you waiting for?' But they were cuddling and kissing someone on the examining table and saying, 'Goodbye Nellie, we will always love you!' and crying a lot.

It was really confusing. And then when they finally left, hugging each other all the time, I had a look at the table and saw a little white dog lying there that looked just like me.

Somebody over here later on explained to me that that was me, but surely that can't be. I mean, how can I be in two places at once?

Anyway, I raced after my parents as they were walking down the road, crying like mad, and I just didn't understand why they couldn't see me because I was right there with them and feeling *soooo* much better.

And then I realised that nobody had opened the door for me, and that I could go anywhere I wanted to without any effort and pain. Not like before. More like, you want to be somewhere, and hey presto, you're there.

I immediately zoomed off to visit Auntie Dee and Uncle Vini to let them know that I was fine. My uncle was sitting in a chair half asleep and I swear he got a glimpse of me.

He later sent Mummy this message: '*I saw Nelson. I fell asleep and he was sitting at my feet near the computer. He looked at me and grinned. As I called out 'Nelson, Nelson', he faded away and I woke up with the taste of his breath in my mouth*'.

That's because I licked him across the face and mouth for good measure, like I always did, and he remembered what that tasted like.

Like I said before, I can't tell you much about what

119

happened next because it's not allowed, but I know now that I died that day. For you. Not for me. I'm here and very much alive. And I'm free. So I get to go everywhere I want to. Any time I want to. Which basically means I'm checking out all the places I know and love. Oh, and I get to hang out with my parents all the time if I want to.

My dad is finally writing music again. When I was still alive my mum always wanted him to write a composition especially for me. But then when I died, my parents realised that I live on in so many of his pieces already. There is one piece of music in particular my parents secretly call 'Nellie's lullaby'. It's hidden in Papá's new *Old World Concerto* for cello. See if you can spot it.

And in his *Christmas Concerto* you can hear me running around at times because I was still alive when he wrote it. And because I was sitting right next to him when he composed it, a part of my spirit must have somehow crept in and stayed.

In the days after I died, my mum wrote a poem about me. It goes like this:

Nelson

A town. A street. A house.
Your town. Your street. Your home.
A window, always framing you, looking out to sea.

Breathe in. Breathe out. Involuntarily.
Without thought or effort.
Today.
Tomorrow…

Tomorrow you will learn that death, not space,
is the final frontier and no amount of guessing,
hoping or fervently believing makes it any easier
a pill to swallow if you are the one left standing
this side of the divide.

Eyes closed, my outstretched hand touches the
empty space and recoils from the impossibility of
you not being here anymore.

My brain can't wrap itself around the unfathomable
immensity of the thought that yesterday, just one tiny,
little day away, you were still mine to hold.

And just like that your mind becomes a battlefield
where a million happy memories will claw at
your heart and try to rip the good times out.

We all know death on paper only.

I AM NELSON

Until it stares you in the face and punches your heart out.
Until you wish you really could drown in your
sea of tears.
And you realise that 'never, ever again' is a damn long
time.

Don't think, don't think!
Because if you do, you're doomed.
You'll notice the absence of everything that was.
A vacuum so vast you can never fully fathom it.

So, do! Whatever....
And walk! Wherever...

And breathe... in... and out... voluntarily...
not really wanting to...
Just going through the motions.

I am washing your things.
To get rid of the pain you left behind.

I'm ironing your blankets.
Which is pointless, because you won't be needing
them anymore.

I'm reluctantly cleaning the house.
But carefully avoiding to wipe the armrest of the sofa
that was your favourite spot, for fear of erasing the tiny
specks of moisture that landed there the very last time you
sneezed.

And I am dreading having to empty the vacuum bag.
Because it contains the last of your hairs.

*And it breaks my heart into thousands of tiny sharp
piercing pieces to know that slowly step by step I am
erasing your presence, until there is no physical evidence
left that you were ever part of my reality.
Until nothing is left of you but a painful memory of what
was.*

*So back to hopes and dreams.
And clinging on for dear life to the thought that maybe,
just maybe, one day we will meet again.*

*A town. A street. A house.
And an empty window staring out to sea.*

You know, the funny thing was that when Mummy finally did clean my sofa, she found that she didn't feel me less afterwards. She cried a lot when she did it, but afterwards I heard her telling Auntie Dee that she felt as if she had only erased my pain and not my presence.

Well of course not. I am still here. Oh, and the spots on the armrest of the sofa I had made by sneezing, mysteriously came back. Even though she had cleaned and oiled it thoroughly. Hehe.

Chapter 11

LOOSE ENDS

A little while ago my parents flew to North America to witness the world premiere of Papá's *Bohemian Concerto*. It is a piano concerto and my dad describes it like this: *'It is the musical illustration of a passionate life full of ups and downs, highs and lows, hopes and dreams, near misses and silver linings. On and on it goes, from one extreme to the next and back again; from happiness to pain, from desperation to hope, from fast to slow, only to pick up again when you think it's all over. It is an interpretation of, and homage to, an artistic life lived to the full without any safety nets.'*

I can tell you that it sounds exactly like that. It's the story of our lives really, and I know the music well because I sat on Mummy's lap most of the time, whenever my dad wanted us to listen to what he had written.

Anyway, when it was finally performed for the first time, I went with my parents to witness it. Normally dogs would not be allowed in a concert hall, but I can go anywhere now because for most people I'm invisible. Also, my mum took a bit of my hair with her in her purse, to make it easier for me to find them, since I had never been to America before.

The concert was really special and beautiful, with a huge orchestra playing, and I saw many people crying. And at the end they all stood up like one and clapped and shouted, which made my parents very happy.

But I still prefer the time when it was just the three of us, up in Papá's studio, with the music filling the whole room, and me sitting on Mummy's lap, while she was crying softly into my fur because she was moved by Papá's beautiful music. And all the while the music was playing, she stroked and hugged and kissed me, and then, right at the end, Papá would lean over and hug and kiss us both.

Right after my parents went to North America, they flew to Argentina in South America, to visit Auntie

Pachy. Of course, originally they had planned to visit her AND Grandma Olga, but unfortunately life decided once more to put a spanner in the works.

And so, just two mere months before they were meant to meet again, Grandma Olga died, because she just couldn't hang on to life any longer. And believe me, she tried!

The last thing she said to my parents on the phone, was 'Not long now!', meaning 'Until we meet again!'. But it wasn't to be, and so my parents got to meet only her ashes.

Now that she's over here and feeling well again, Grandma Olga had a right laugh about what happened next. That's because she watched my parents scatter her ashes together with my Auntie Pachy. And what a right mess that turned out to be. I'll only say 'extremely windy day' and you can imagine the rest.

They all ended up with bits of Grandma Olga on their clothes, inside their shoes and even under their fingernails. She even popped up in Mummy's and Auntie Pachy's bras.

Grandma Olga laughed so loud, she could almost be heard on the other side. And she loved every minute of it, because that's just the kind of person she is.

Auntie Pachy has two cats that I would have gladly chased around, had I still been able to. Just before my parents left for home once more, I heard my dad whisper to one of them, who is fifteen years old: 'Goodbye Pushu, have a happy rest of your life. And when you finally go, please say hello to Nelson. He is also white like you, so you will easily be able to recognise him.'

Now, whilst I appreciate the sentiment, I really hope for her sake that she doesn't. Never was particularly keen on cats, even though my mum always had the sneaking suspicion that I had been their first cat in my previous life.

I'm not saying anything.

Now time is ticking by, and the novelty of being here has seriously started to wear off, I find I miss my parents more and more.

I miss so many things! My morning routine: Papá getting up early to compose, which means extra time with Mummy in bed. Then, when he brings her a cup of tea, I take care no liberties are being taken and I get to kiss him too. His chin is rough, but not as hairy as my bottom, and sometimes I lick them both, one after the other.

Mind you, I have to make sure he isn't watching, otherwise Papá won't let me lick his face.

I miss my house, especially lounging on my sofa with the sun shining on my belly, until it's almost too hot to bear. I miss watching the street and the sea from my window, and making sure that whoever passes by knows that I am in charge of it all. And don't you dare wave at me, or else I'll tell you what I think about it.

I miss seeing Auntie Marina and Uncle Richard on Sundays, hanging out with Auntie Dee, and sharing my food with Uncle Vini.

I miss my favourite toys, especially Hugo and my beloved Clara, who Papá gave me on my last birthday, and who I made sure had one leg missing just like me.

I miss the way my mum would always pass the hair dryer backwards and forwards between my fur and her hair, and sharing tons of carrots at night on the sofa with Papá.

I miss barbecues on the hill, wading through all the puddles and creeks in the Country Park, and marking the trees on my favourite walks through the woods. Sometimes my dad would mark them too, but he was never quite as prolific as me.

And I miss running. Running is the best! Any time and everywhere, but always making sure that everyone knows I'm the one in charge. How? Simple – quick turn of the head, grabbing the lead firmly between your teeth, and PULL! That way everyone knows who's leading who. And then running like the wind, pulling whoever holds the other end of the lead along with you.

I also miss playing pull with whoever happened to come over for a visit, whether they wanted to or not. I could have happily played pull for hours on end, but woe betide anyone who didn't bear rule number one in mind and dared to touch my back or bottom. Towards the end of my life most people knew, but just in case, my parents always made sure to tell visitors to keep their hands to themselves.

My mum always used to say that on the outside I was a mixture between Jack Russell and Corgi, but on the inside I was at times a right little Shih Tzu.

And by the way she pronounced it, everybody knew exactly just what she meant. And it sure wasn't the breed she was referring to.

She used to say it especially when I had one of my many sudden mood swings. Mummy says my eyes would change from warm chocolate brown to demon jet black in an instant, and I would get *that look* in my eyes, the one that let everybody know that I meant business. You know, the look that snarled 'STEP AWAY NOW!! OR ELSE!'

Before my mum became an actress, she used to be a dancer. That's why she still does a lot of her exercises to keep flexible every other evening or so in our living room. And of course I always got to do them with her. When I was still a puppy, she used to put her feet under my tummy and push me right up into the air and towards the ceiling, which was great fun and a little bit scary, too. And later, when I didn't want her to do that anymore because it wasn't very dignified, she used to do the same thing with my favourite ball, and I got to jump up and try to snatch it away from her. I miss that, too.

When I was younger and happened to be lying on her lap, my mum sometimes used to flip me backwards, so that I would come to rest on my back or side, with my head firmly tucked under her chin. I would always protest when she did it, and as I got older didn't let her do it anymore because, as you know, I like to be in control. But secretly I loved it a lot, and now I miss it very much.

And now that it is almost Christmas again, I miss the tree my mum puts up, and walking past Heloir and nipping him on the sly. Yes, I know, I said I didn't mind him that much, but I couldn't let the side down either now, could I?!

Oh, and I WISH I could have another advent calendar! Last year my mum bought one for me for the very first time ever. She almost didn't, because she felt a bit silly buying one for me, and also doggie advent calendars don't exactly come cheap. But boy am I glad she did! And so are my parents. I can't begin to tell you how much I loved this new routine.

Every morning my dad would carry the calendar into the bedroom, along with Mummy's good morning tea. And then my parents would open a tiny paper door on it, with lots of yummy treats hidden behind it. Different ones each morning. I could smell them a mile off, and it makes my mouth water even now to think of it. Every day I got more and more excited about my calendar, and Mummy and Papá more worried, because of course they knew that there were only 24 doors to open. And they didn't exactly know how to explain to me that one day this great new game would be over.

As it turned out, I realised what would happen on my own. Firstly, because I'm not dim. And secondly, because I could smell that were fewer and fewer treats hidden behind the doors.

So, after the very last door was opened and I had gulped down my last treat, Papá showed me the empty calendar but he didn't take it away like he had done every morning before. So I ripped it wide open, just to make sure that what my nose had told me was correct, and no more treats were hidden anywhere inside.

What surprised my parents no end, was the fact that come the next morning I didn't get all excited, waiting for the calendar to make a reappearance.

I guess they underestimated my intelligence. Oh, and they did promise me that come next Christmas I would get another one.

But as we all know, that's one promise they don't get to keep.

Chapter 12

NOW

Last night I heard Mummy cry again. It snapped me right back home. She was walking around the living room in the dark, and I heard her whispering, 'I love you, Nellie' and 'Where are you now?' and 'Can you please give me a sign if you're there?' She even whistled the three notes she always used to whistle to call me back when we were out walking in the park. And I was barking at the top of my voice, 'Yes, Mummy, I'm right here!' But she couldn't hear me. And then Papá was holding her and his eyes were wet, too. And for once I wasn't jealous like I used to be. And I didn't even growl like I always used to do every time my dad kissed my mum, just to make sure he didn't take any liberties. Because cuddles and *mimo* were supposed to be only for me.

People over there think my mum has to move on. Funny, because over here they tell me the same. But how can I do that, when my parents miss me so much, and all I want to do is to be back with them again.

The other day I heard Mummy tell someone that she has a Nelson-shaped hole in her heart and that she simply cannot accept that I am really gone.

I heard her say:

'I want him back so badly it hurts. Every tiny little thing is a reminder of him and in my inner eye I see him everywhere. We just spent so much time together and had created so many routines with him, that there is this huge chunk of our lives which is now missing. Our house is completely and utterly empty without him and there are just so many things I miss, big and little.

There's the way he always did things his own way. He was the most intelligent dog I have ever met, and I'm not just saying this because he was our baby.

For example, we used to give him treats during the day when he nudged the cupboard with all his food in it. But then, rather than just give him a treat, we used to hold two treats of different flavours in front of his nose to give him a choice. Now, every other dog I've ever known, would grab the closest one or maybe even try to gobble up both. But not Nelson.

He would first sniff one and then the other, and sometimes repeat the whole procedure, until he was completely sure which one he wanted. Then he would visibly make his choice by nudging the one he wanted with his nose. As soon as it was given to him he would quickly vanish up the stairs to eat it. I remember one time he did this, he must have changed his mind, because halfway up the stairs he turned around and brought his treat back down. Uneaten! And he indicated with his head that he would rather have the other one I was still holding in my hand. He then proceeded to lay choice number one on the floor, take choice number two and vanish upstairs with it.

I have also never seen a dog visibly think things over the way he did. Unfortunately that also made him a bit of a worrier and sometimes he reached the wrong conclusions, just as humans do.

For example, right up to his last major operation, he used to play a lot with his rubber-based toys and favourite balls, as he had done for many years on a daily basis. Yet after his amputation he seemed to associate them with what had happened and almost superstitiously didn't want to touch them anymore. But it definitely wasn't a case of not wanting to play anymore per se. No, he played a lot, but exclusively with toys we had bought him post op.

Nelson also had this amazing way of working things

out. For example, he would normally sleep whenever we watched television because he knew that the things on the screen weren't real. In other words, he knew the difference between a cat in real life and a cat on the television. The former he would chase and have a go at, the latter he would completely ignore. But just occasionally a story would come on that seemed to interest him and he would sit up and listen.

I will never forget, one evening I was watching a programme about the horrific slaughter of hundreds of Native Americans at Wounded Knee, when Nelson all of a sudden sat up. He moved his head from one side to the other, like he always did when he tried to understand what was being said.

Now I should clarify that all the programme showed was a group of Native Americans telling the tragic story of their ancestors. In other words, there was no re-enactment of what had happened, nor any scenes of violence visible on the screen at that time, just a group of people talking about something that had affected them deeply.

That's when all of a sudden Nelson started to howl like a wolf from the bottom of his soul, and his whole demeanour was one of deep anguish. It was the eeriest thing and it convinced me that he really had understood what was being said, rather than react to something he saw.

I also know for a fact, that Nelson knew that it was the remote control that switched the TV on and off. We always had to press it twice; once to switch the dish *connection off and the second time to switch the actual TV set off. Each evening, after the first button was pressed, Nelson would look first at the TV screen, and then pointedly at the remote control and back at the TV again, to make sure the screen went completely blank.'*

More like I had to make sure they did things properly, because if not I would have had the buzzing from the TV in my ears all night long. And of course I knew what was said on the box. Why on Earth wouldn't I??!

My dad remembers stuff about me, too. Like the time, quite a few years ago, when my parents realised they had to rush off to a meeting, just when Mummy had finished serving roast chicken, potatoes and vegetables. They had forgotten the time, but figured they'd be back in half an hour and would simply finish eating their dinner then.

So they left it all on the kitchen table and rushed out of the house. I heard Papá tell someone later that all through the meeting he had been looking forward to eating the rest of his dinner.

Now, I may have mentioned that roast chicken is one of my all-time favourites… Well, at the time my dad was also rather partial to it.

Unfortunately for him though, by the time my parents got back home, all that remained of their dinner were some extremely oily paw prints all across the kitchen table and chairs. Oh, and yes, also on the staircase leading right up to where I was snoozing happily on the sofa.

Took me a while to live that one down. And no food was ever left unattended anywhere after that. Shame!

I know some dates are important because people keep mentioning them like words to remember stuff by. 25/07/2007 for example is the day I was born. 25/04/2008 is the day my parents adopted me, and 24/04/2019 is the day I died. It is also one day before I would have been exactly 11 years with my mum and dad, which they say makes it even more poignant.

And of course Wednesdays will never be the same again, because I died on a Wednesday.

It is now exactly 38 Wednesdays since I died, and my story is almost told. I sure will miss this time writing it with my mum. And I know she will, too. It was almost as if we were back together again.

My mum says, in folklore there is a belief that the dead can come back briefly in the form of a bird, to say hello or goodbye to the living. That freaked my Uncle Richard right out because he thought she meant possession. But it's not like that. It's more like hitching a ride. I mean when you fly away on holiday to somewhere, you don't all of a sudden become an airplane. No, you just hitch a ride, and when you look out of the window it's still you inside the airplane, having a peak at what's going on down below. Same with the birds and the dead. I tried it once and let me tell you, it really works. For the briefest of times I was inside a magpie and I swear my parents saw me.

My mum is also convinced that she saw my brother Oscar, who died a few years before I came along, once after he died. He hitched a ride with a crow that time. And the crow walked right up to my mum and even started to limp, just like Oscar used to do when he was still alive. I've recently met Oscar over here because he loves my parents, too, and checks up on them from time to time. Only now he doesn't limp anymore and he isn't crooked anymore either. And he's almost forgotten his horrible time with the man who beat and crippled him so badly, before he was rescued and my parents took him in.

Even when I'm not hitching a ride with anyone, I still hang around to see what's going on. From time to time I check if my toys are still in the basket where I last left them, and I'm very pleased to say that they are. I only regret that I can't pick them up anymore. And believe me, I have tried. Mummy is daring me all the time to do so, but my teeth go right through them, which we both find extremely frustrating.

Apart from my toys, some things have changed in my house. I saw my mum emptying out my drawer in the hallway, where my poo bags and my lead and all my harnesses used to be. I didn't like her doing that really, but now Papá is using it for his gloves and hats, so I guess that's ok.

And my cupboard in the kitchen, where my food used to be, is now half empty too. I always used to nose the door open in my desperation to get at my treats, which made my dad laugh a lot, so he encouraged it.

The box with some of my clothes is still in there; like my lovely green parka with the hood for when it snowed or rained, and the yellow harness my parents got me because it was soft and didn't hurt my belly. But all my food is gone, apart from one tin my mum just cannot give away. Just in case.

All my tins and treats went to a charity, because I don't need them anymore. And some of my other stuff is now in the attic. Like my travel bed, the one I used until right at the end because it was my favourite one, as it had always carried me places, but most importantly it had always brought me home again. My parents will never give that away I think, because it meant so much to me.

My pram is also still on the attic. Too many memories around that one, too. Most of my pillow cases my mum gave to Auntie Pachy, so Pushu can use them because she also has white fur that clings to everything. Also, Mummy likes to think that that way part of me lives on with Auntie Pachy.

In our bedroom not much has changed. My proper bed is still in there, even though I stopped using it when I got seriously ill at the end. Call me superstitious, but I never felt much like using it after I lost my leg and preferred to sleep in my soft travel bed in the hallway upstairs, just outside our bedroom. That and in my parents' bed of course. But like I said, they move around so much, I never really managed to stay with them the whole night through. But I used it as my day bed a lot, which made my mum smile.

My proper bed still looks the same way it always did, with my favourite white blanket draped over the back. I wish I could snuggle down on it, just to see if it still feels the same. Only then my ashes would get in the way. My parents kept them because everyone who touched them said they weirdly feel like me. So now they can't get rid of them. And after what happened with Grandma Olga's ashes, even less so.

I don't really mind. I doesn't really matter, as I'm here and don't need that old body anymore, because my new one is so much better now. I've got my four legs back and no boil or sore or cancer in sight.

But I'm beginning to wonder what's going to happen next. Lately I've been getting this urgent feeling that it's almost time now, and I've been wondering if my parents are hiding right behind the white light I can see in the distance.

My mum believes, that if you love someone an awful lot, and they love you right back the exact same way, your souls become entwined and are forever linked together by an invisible band. That way you will be always able to find each other again, and all you need to do when you are lost, is to close your eyes and trust the link to pull you right back to the person you love.

I have a feeling that she might be right. That's what I am counting on anyway.

On my 12th birthday, the one I never had, my mum and dad put the picture of me that my Uncle Vini had painted, on the kitchen chair along with my favourite yellow ball.

On the table in front of it, they put a birthday candle in a piece of ham and cheese, and a big yellow balloon with white letters saying 'Happy Birthday'. Just like we always used to do when I was still around.

Truth be told, I could have done without the balloon. I never liked them much, because sooner or later they pop and hurt my ears. But I put up with them because my mum always puts balloons on the table for birthdays and it makes her happy.

Then my parents lit the candle and sang 'Happy Birthday, Nellie', and they cried, because they wanted me to sit on the chair instead of my picture.

And then Papá told me to make a wish, because everyone knows that birthday wishes come true.

Which isn't completely true, because Mummy was wishing with all her might on the day of her own birthday that I would get well again, and that didn't happen. Well, at least not in the sense she meant it to. But I guess, maybe that's because it wasn't meant to be, because we all have to die sometime.

But anyway, when my dad said 'Make a wish!' to me that day, I just knew exactly what my wish would be.

And so I wished with all my heart.

145

Chapter 13

WISHFUL THINKING?

It was a beautiful day and the little puppy sniffed the crisp spring air.

It knew exactly what it wanted. It always had. There was a distinct, almost human smile on its roguish little face as it was staring at the door. Everything was going to be alright at last.

Because it just knew that today was the day…

THE END?

(cue music: *Still Life Goes On* from the album *Sentimental Journey* by Polo Piatti)

MY PHOTO GALLERY

Hello! This is me guarding my window. Somebody has to…

Selfie

Enough already!

My very first birthday - with my mum

Early days. Getting to know my mum

Another birthday - this time with my dad

My first birthday hamburger. One of many...

Sticks…   … and pebbles

Counting my celery bits. Just in case someone stole any…

Don't you dare touch my last bit of carrot!

Snoozing with my mum

Watching telly with my dad

Listening to music

With Uncle Vini…   … and Auntie Dee

Christmas dinner with Uncle Richard and Auntie Marina

With my dad and Grandma Olga

Ok. So, yes, I *was* contemplating having a go at Auntie Pachy…

Tea break with my mum, Auntie Pachy and Grandma Olga

On the road again

I was having great fun on holiday…

… until I spotted the scary grass monster

See how tiny our tent was!

Having a rest on the endless
South Coastal path

Enough is enough!

And that's how you keep your paws warm in the snow

Having fun with my dad

Don't say a word! With my mum on Halloween

My Pirate Day outfit

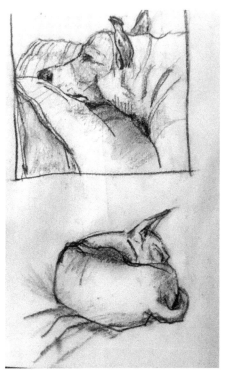

Some drawings Grandma C made of me...

... whilst I was snoozing

Exercising with my mum

Posing in front of my portrait

Not amused!

The long drive home after my amputation

Getting used to life with three legs

Outing in my pram… no comment…

Working with my dad

With Clara, my birthday
surprise

Had to make sure she looked
just like me

Sitting down for dinner

Running on three legs

Quick lick to make sure my mum doesn't have dirt on her face

Good night!

AUTHOR'S NOTE

At first I didn't want to write an author's note at all. Partly because this is my first (and so far only) book and it just felt a bit pretentious to call myself an author after only one go at writing, but mainly because this is really more Nelson's book than mine. But then I reminded myself how much I personally love to read a note at the end of a story to find out how it came to be written. So here goes:

Nelson died on 24th April 2019 just after 12pm, having finally lost his battle with cancer.

A few weeks after his death, while I was busy going to pieces over his loss, I suddenly felt this almighty nudge to write his story. At first I resisted because – apart from poetry and the odd audition piece and short script – I had never written anything. But, as you know by now, Nelson is tenacious and just kept pushing, and so I finally gave in.

Over the next few months, whenever I had a spare moment, I would write. And whenever I didn't, I would feel this pressing urgency to get on with it. And so I did.

A lot of people assumed I was writing for therapeutic reasons, but it wasn't really like that. It was the oddest thing. The words just kept popping into my brain at the weirdest moments – especially while I was cleaning or doing something equally mundane.

It wasn't easy to write it all down because I had to relive all the harrowing moments over and over again, but at the same time it was also lovely to feel Nelson close and to be reunited with all the good memories.

And when it was all finally done I thought that I would go back to what I normally do, and that my stint at writing was over.

But the funny thing was... more words kept popping into my head...

(So I guess, it looks like Nelson will have the last word yet.)

Hastings, December 2020

ACKNOWLEDGMENTS

When I had finally finished writing Nelson's story, I gave it to his extended family and friends to read first. I was really grateful that they did, and very touched indeed when they told me they had laughed and cried their way through the story they all know so well.

Thanks for all your helpful comments and suggestions, but most of all, thanks for being there, before and after, and for not forgetting your most unruly nephew. It means a lot to me.

I would also like to thank Claire Gillman for editorially assessing my manuscript and for not tearing it to bits. I really enjoyed our chat – here's to synchronicities! – but I feel rather guilty for not implementing all the suggested changes – blame it on Nelson, he just wouldn't budge.

Another special thank-you goes out to Fiona Wilson for proof reading and casting her eagle eye over my manuscript, and for getting rid of all those pesky, superfluous commas and other mistakes in such a thorough way. Oh, and for introducing me to the weird and wonderful world of the en–dash.

Thanks also to all the vets in Nelson's life for looking after him the way you did – even when he emphatically didn't want you to – and for trying to save him.

Another big thank-you goes to Paul Knight who very kindly offered to improve the quality of the photos in the *My Photo Gallery* section, when I got rather stuck trying to figure out how to calculate their DPIs and how to 'flatten' them – and for diligently disinfecting the memory stick before drop-off during the second Covid-19 pandemic lockdown.

And of course a massive thank-you to all of you out there for reading Nelson's story. Because by doing so you are keeping him alive.

And last, but never, ever least, thank you to my husband Polo Piatti for being *The One* and for sharing this – and every other – journey with me.

And Nelson would like to say:
(… FINALLY she lets me speak…)
Thanks *soooooooo* much to all my aunties and uncles who made my life such fun! You were very special to me and I miss you very much.

But watch this space: you just *might* haven't seen the last of me yet…

PS: Rule Number One still applies. Just in case you were wondering.

ABOUT THE AUTHOR

Martina Mars is an actress and former dancer and as such has had all the usual – and unusual – daytime jobs in her time. She lives with her husband in East Sussex in the UK. This is her first book, although Nelson is currently nudging her mightily to write some more...

FREE MUSIC DOWNLOAD

As you all know, Nelson used to listen to his dad's music a lot. One of the pieces, *Still Life Goes On* from the album *Sentimental Journey*, became the soundtrack to this book.

If you would like to listen to it, you can get your own **FREE music download** of the track here:

www.martinamars.com/free-download

Printed in Great Britain
by Amazon